LEAD POISONING PREVENTION:
DIRECTORY OF STATE CONTACTS 1993

Compiled by

Doug Farquhar
Linda South

State Issues and Policy Analysis Program

National Conference of State Legislatures
William T. Pound, Executive Director

1560 Broadway, Suite 700
Denver, Colorado 80202-5140

444 North Capitol Street, N.W., Suite 515
Washington, D.C. 20001

May 1993

Lead Poisoning Prevention: Directory of State Contacts 1993
is printed on recycled paper.

Disclaimer

Information in this directory was compiled with a grant from an agency
of the United States of America. Neither the United States nor any of its
employees, contractors, subcontractors, nor their employees make any
warranty, expressed or implied; or assume any legal liability or
responsibility for third party's use of any information, apparatus,
product, or process disclosed in this report; or for the results of such use,
or represent that its use by such third party would not infringe on
privately owned rights.

TABLE OF CONTENTS

The *Lead Poisoning Prevention: Directory of State Contacts 1993* identifies the main contacts in the health, environmental, and occupational safety and health agencies in each state on lead poisoning prevention. Information for this directory came from contacts within state lead programs or from other sources confirmed by state lead contacts. We appreciate and acknowledge the time and effort given by every person who assisted in the project, especially the overall lead contacts who reviewed the final draft of the directory. Production of this directory is part of a project to assist states in reducing lead hazards.

Karen Fisher edited the publication and Rena Roybal provided computer support.

NCSL greatly appreciates any updates or comments about the directory. Please write or call:

Lead Hazards Project
National Conference of State Legislatures
1560 Broadway, Suite 700
Denver, Colorado 80202
303/830-2200 Fax: 303/863-8003

Lead poisoning is the most common and most preventable environmental disease of young children, according to the Centers for Disease Control and Prevention (CDC). Recent studies show that even minimal levels of lead absorbed into the blood of children under six years of age can cause long-term damage to the central nervous system and can significantly impair intelligence and neurobehavioral functions. Because of these studies, a reemergence of lead poisoning prevention activities has occurred in both state and federal government.

Heightened concern with lead poisoning creates a need to identify persons responsible for the various prevention activities within states. This directory identifies those persons and their respective programs and activities. Each state section lists the main state agency contacts for that state for 19 types of lead poisoning prevention activities (Table 1 defines and describes these activities). Short summaries highlight any other special features of state programs, such as whether lead poisoning is a reportable disease; how a program handles abatement; environmental assessment or case management; sources of grant funding; or other activities.

Table 2 charts the activities or program categories listed by the contacts for their state. Besides program activities, state contacts were asked about specifics of their programs, such as whether a license is required before using abatement equipment, whether the state approves or certifies training courses, whether the state requires screening for lead, when inspections are required and what technology is allowed. These questions are explained in Table 1.

Every state has some activities to address lead poisoning prevention (see Table 2). Forty-six states listed an overall lead contact, and 35 identified an environmental contact. Screening contacts were identified in 41 states, and screening is required in 25. Forty states listed a contact to do surveillance activities, collecting data to identify cases of elevated blood lead levels. Thirty-five states listed abatement/standards and enforcement contacts, 18 have adopted standards for abatement and remediation, and eight require some sort of license to perform abatement activities. Twenty-one identified a contact for the training/certification/accreditation category. Public outreach contacts were listed in 41 states. Thirty-nine states identified medical laboratory contacts, and 33 listed an environmental laboratory contact. Thirty-three states have received grants, and 21 finance local and community lead projects. In 29 states, lead poisoning is a reportable disease.

INTRODUCTION

The directory was compiled initially in January and February 1992. The 1993 directory is based on contacts made with each state in February 1993 to update and compile additional data about state programs. Comments and corrections received from the states were incorporated into the final draft.

TABLE 1
Program Categories and State Activities for
Lead Poisoning Prevention
(as listed in the survey)

The following describes the various program categories and lists the questions as they appeared on the survey. Each state contact was asked to mark the categories that best identify the official function and answer all questions related to that category. The number listed next to the program categories and questions corresponds with the numbers listed in the table. The answers from each state contact are indicated in Table 2. In the table, a dot symbolizes an affirmative answer.

1. **Overall Lead Contact**—identifies the main contact for the state, either the program administrator or the director of an agency. Questions regarding the development or structure of a state's lead program should be directed to this person.

2. **Abatement/Standards and Enforcement**—identifies the person responsible for any abatement activities and/or the development of abatement standards and the enforcement of those standards.

2a. Can the state require an abatement or remediation of a lead hazard?

2b. Has the state adopted standards for abatement or remediation?

2c. Does the state have or provide equipment for abatement or remediation?

3. **Training/Certification/Accreditation**—identifies the person who oversees or may receive the responsibility of training or certification of abatement professionals. Many states do not have such programs, but have identified potential persons or programs to handle such activities if or when they develop.

3a. Does the state approve or certify training providers?

3b. Does the state approve or certify professions or disciplines to perform lead abatement or inspection activities?

3c. Does the state allow for reciprocity with other states?

4. **Financing Projects**—identifies the person who is responsible for providing financial support to local projects or agencies.

4a. Does the state finance or provide grants for local or community lead projects?

5. **Grant(s) Recipient**—identifies whether that person's program has been awarded grant funding and/or if that person is responsible for proposing grant applications for that program.

6. **Medical Contact**—identifies the medical consultant for the state's lead prevention programs.

7. **Screening**—identifies the person who is responsible for blood lead screening activities within the state.

7a. Does the state require screening of children for lead poisoning?

8. **Inspections**—identifies the person responsible for follow-up inspections for areas or buildings found to have high contents of lead.

8a. Can the state require an inspection to determine sources of lead?

8b. What technology is used to perform inspections for lead?

9. **Laboratories-Environmental**—identifies the person or director responsible for environmental lead sample analysis, such as soil, paint chip, or building samples.

9a. Do state labs analyze environmental lead samples?

10. **Laboratories-Medical**—identifies the person or director responsible for blood lead content analysis. Some state laboratories do not have these capabilities and send their samples to private labs or out-of-state. Some states require labs to report any elevated blood lead levels.

10a. Are state labs capable of analyzing blood lead samples?

11. **Surveillance**—identifies the person responsible for collecting and identifying persons with elevated blood lead if lead is a reportable disease in their state.

11a. Is lead poisoning a reportable disease?

11b. At what level is it reportable ($\mu g/dL$)?

12. **Public Outreach**—identifies the person responsible for education and outreach to the public and local health, educational, and environmental agencies for their program.

13. **Public Housing**—identifies the person within a state's public housing agency responsible for lead activities. Most public housing agencies are not at the state level.

14. **Environmental (General)**—identifies the main contact for environmental lead programs, either a program manager or director.

15. **National Drinking Water Regulation for Lead (NDWRL)**—identifies the person designated as responsible for the implementation of this federal program. This person usually oversees all drinking water activities for the state.

16. **Lead Contamination Control Act (LCCA)**—identifies the person responsible for implementing the LCCA, which requires lead be removed from plumbing in schools. Often this duty falls upon the person responsible for the state's plumbing regulations.

17. **Disposal**—identifies the person responsible for any disposal or RCRA requirements regarding lead. Many states list lead as a regulated waste but few have rules specifically dealing with lead.

17a. Is lead considered a hazardous waste?

17b. Has the state received authorization to administer the federal Resource Conservation and Recovery Act (RCRA) program?

18. **Soils**—identifies the person who is responsible for regulations concerning lead in soils. Few states designate such a person.

18a. Does the state have a standard for lead in soils? What level is considered a health risk?

18b. Can the state mandate abatement of lead-contaminated soils?

19. **Occupational Safety and Health**—identifies the person within the state OSHA responsible for any elevated blood lead in workers or any lead hazards in an occupational setting.

19a. At what lead level does the state mandate a response for adults in an occupational setting?

TABLE 2
Lead Activities Under State Programs

The following charts indicate the program categories identified by the state contacts and the activities related to those programs. A dot indicates an affirmative answer.

LEAD ACTIVITIES UNDER STATE PROGRAMS

		AL	AK	AZ	AR	CA	CO	CT	DE	FL
1	**Overall Lead Contact**	●		●	●	●	●	●	●	●
2	**Abatement/Stnds&Enforce**	●	●	●		●		●	●	
a	Abatement Required			●					●	
b	Abatement Standards			●				●	●	
c	Equipment for Abatement	●				●			●	
3	**Training/Cert/Accreditation**	●				●		●	●	
a	Certified Training					●		●		
b	Certification of Professionals	●	●					●		
c	Reciprocity									
4	**Financing Projects**							●	●	
a	Financing Local Projects					●		●	●	
5	**Grant(s) Recipient**	●				●		●	●	
6	**Medical Contact**	●	●	●	●	●			●	●
7	**Screening Contact**	●		●	●	●		●	●	●
a	Screening Required	●				●			●	●
8	**Inspection Contact**	●		●	●	●		●	●	●
a	Inspection Required	●		●		●			●	●
b	Technology Used	x	a	o		x a			a	a
9	**Laboratories--Environmental**	●	●	●		●		●	●	●
a	State Labs Analysis					●				●

Program Categories are Listed in Bold
Activities Under Those Programs are Indented
● Indicates an affirmative answer
x XRF
a Atomic Absorption Spectrometry
s Sodium Sulfide
o Other (see state section)

	GA	HI	ID	IL	IN	IA	KS	KY	LA	ME	MD	MA	MI	MN	MS	MO
1	•	•	•	•	•	•	•	•	•	•	•	•	•	•	•	•
2				•			•	•	•	•	•	•	•	•		•
a				•					•	•	•				•	
b				•					•	•	•	•			•	
c				•	•				•	•	•	•			•	
3				•		•				•	•	•		•		
a				•						•	•	•				
b				•						•	•	•				
c										•						
4	•			•	•	•	•			•	•	•	•			
a				•	•	•		•		•	•	•	•			
5		•	•	•	•	•	•	•		•	•	•	•	•		•
6			•	•	•	•	•	•	•	•	•	•				
7		•		•	•	•	•	•	•	•	•	•	•	•	•	
a					•			•	•			•	•		•	
8		•	•	•	•		•	•	•	•		•	•	•		
a		•	•	•	•		•	•	•	•	•	•	•			
b		o		x a	xao	xas		x	x a	x a	xao	xao	x a			
9					•	•	•	•	•	•	•	•	•		•	•
a				•	•	•		•	•			•	•	•		•

Program Categories are Listed in Bold

Activities Under Those Programs are Indented

- Indicates an affirmative answer

x XRF

a Atomic Absorption Spectrometry

s Sodium Sulfide

o Other (see state section)

		MT	NE	NV	NH	NJ	NM	NY	NC	ND
1	**Overall Lead Contact**	●	●		●	●	●	●	●	●
2	**Abatement/Stnds&Enforce**	●		●	●	●		●	●	●
a	Abatement Required				●	●	●	●	●	●
b	Abatement Standards				●	●	●	●	●	●
c	Equipment for Abatement	●			●	●		●	●	
3	**Training/Cert/Accreditation**				●	●		●		
a	Certified Training									
b	Certification of Professionals									
c	Reciprocity									
4	**Financing Projects**	●	●			●		●		
a	Financing Local Projects		●			●		●		●
5	**Grant(s) Recipient**	●		●	●	●	●	●		
6	**Medical Contact**		●	●	●	●	●	●		●
7	**Screening Contact**	●	●	●	●	●	●	●	●	●
a	Screening Required	●	●			●	●		●	●
8	**Inspection Contact**	●	●	●	●	●	●	●	●	●
a	Inspection Required	●			●	●	●	●		●
b	Technology Used	x a								
9	**Laboratories--Environmental**	●			●	●	●	●	●	●
a	State Labs Analysis	●	●		●	●	●	●	●	●

Program Categories are Listed in Bold
Activities Under Those Programs are Indented
● Indicates an affirmative answer
x XRF
a Atomic Absorption Spectrometry
s Sodium Sulfide
o Other (see state section)

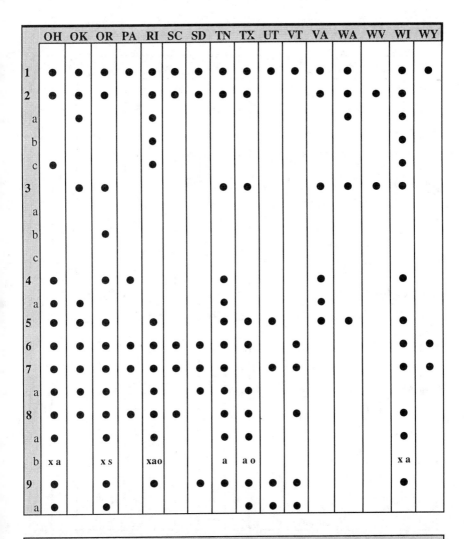

	OH	OK	OR	PA	RI	SC	SD	TN	TX	UT	VT	VA	WA	WV	WI	WY
1	●	●	●	●	●	●	●	●	●	●	●	●	●		●	●
2	●	●	●		●	●	●	●	●			●	●	●	●	
a		●			●								●		●	
b					●										●	
c	●				●										●	
3		●	●					●	●			●	●	●	●	
a																
b			●													
c																
4	●		●	●				●				●			●	
a	●	●						●				●				
5	●	●	●		●			●	●	●		●	●		●	
6	●	●	●	●	●	●	●	●	●		●				●	●
7	●	●	●	●	●	●	●	●		●	●				●	●
a	●	●	●		●		●	●	●							
8	●	●	●	●	●	●		●	●		●				●	
a	●		●		●			●	●					●		
b	x a		x s		xao			a	a o						x a	
9	●	●			●	●	●	●		●	●				●	
a	●		●					●		●	●					

Program Categories are Listed in Bold

Activities Under Those Programs are Indented

● Indicates an affirmative answer

x XRF

a Atomic Absorption Spectrometry

s Sodium Sulfide

o Other (see state section)

		AL	AK	AZ	AR	CA	CO	CT	DE	FL
10	**Laboratories--Medical**	●	●	●	●	●			●	●
a	State Labs Analysis					●				●
11	**Surveillance Contact**	●		●		●	●	●	●	●
a	Lead Poisoning Reportable		●	●		●	●	●	●	●
b	Level Reportable µg/dL		25	25		25	10	*	25	25
c	CDC Grant					●		●	●	●
12	**Public Outreach Contact**	●		●	●	●	●	●	●	
13	**Public Housing Contact**				●	●				
14	**Environmental (General)**	●			●	●	●	●	●	●
15	**NDWRL Contact**	●	●	●	●	●	●	●	●	●
16	**LCCA Contact**	●		●	●	●			●	●
17	**Disposal Contact**	●		●		●			●	
a	Lead Considered Hazardous		●			●				
b	RCRA Delegated					●				
18	**Soil Contact**	●	●						●	
a	Soil Standard (ppm)					1000				
b	Abatement Required					●				
19	**OSHA Contact**	●	●	●		●	●	●		
a	Blood Level/Actionable		25			40				

Program Categories are Listed in Bold

Activities Under Those Programs are Indented

● Indicates an affirmative answer

* Refer to State Section

	GA	HI	ID	IL	IN	IA	KS	KY	LA	ME	MD	MA	MI	MN	MS	MO
10				●	●	●	●	●	●	●	●	●		●		●
a				●	●	●				●			●	●		●
11		●	●	●	●	●	●	●		●	●	●	●	●		
a		●		●		●				●	●	●	●	●		
b		all			21	10				20	20	25		all	all	
c		●		●						●	●	●		●		
12	●	●	●	●	●	●		●		●	●	●	●	●	●	●
13					●	●										
14	●	●	●		●		●	●	●	●	●	●	●			●
15	●			●	●	●			●	●	●	●	●			●
16	●			●	●	●	●		●	●	●	●	●			●
17	●			●						●	●		●	●	●	●
a	●										●		●	●		
b	●										●		●	●		
18	●	●		●						●	●		●	●	●	●
a		400	1000								1000		400	300		
b									●	●			●	●		
19			●	●							●	●	●			
a													15	>50		

Program Categories are Listed in Bold

Activities Under Those Programs are Indented

● Indicates an affirmative answer

* Refer to State Section

		MT	NE	NV	NH	NJ	NM	NY	NC	ND
10	**Laboratories--Medical**	●	●		●	●	●	●	●	●
a	State Labs Analysis	●	●		●	●	●	●	●	●
11	**Surveillance**	●			●	●	●	●	●	●
a	Lead Poisoning Reportable				●	●	●	●		●
b	Level Reportable µg/dL		10		25	25		10	25	>10
c	CDC Grant						●	●		
12	**Public Outreach**	●		●	●	●	●	●	●	
13	**Public Housing**									
14	**Environmental (General)**		●			●	●	●		●
15	**NDWRL**	●	●		●		●	●	●	●
16	**LCCA**	●	●				●	●	●	
17	**Disposal**	●			●	●	●		●	●
a	Lead Considered Hazardous				●		●		●	●
b	RCRA Delegated				●		●		●	
18	**Soil**				●	●	●	●		●
a	Soil Standard (ppm)						500		500	
b	Abatement Required				●		●		●	
19	**OSHA**	●		●	●	●		●	●	
a	Blood Level/Actionable			40	40	25				

Program Categories are Listed in Bold

Activities Under Those Programs are Indented

● Indicates an affirmative answer

∗ Refer to State Section

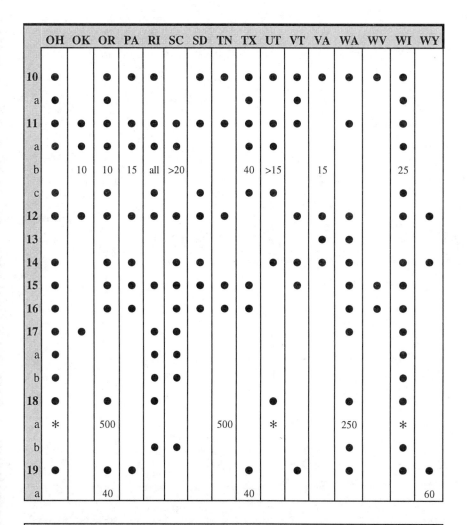

	OH	OK	OR	PA	RI	SC	SD	TN	TX	UT	VT	VA	WA	WV	WI	WY
10	●		●	●	●		●	●	●	●	●	●	●	●	●	
a	●		●					●			●				●	
11	●	●	●	●	●	●	●	●	●	●	●		●		●	
a	●	●	●	●	●	●			●	●					●	
b		10	10	15	all	>20			40	>15		15			25	
c	●		●		●			●		●					●	
12	●	●	●	●	●	●	●	●			●	●	●		●	●
13											●	●				
14	●		●	●		●	●			●	●	●	●		●	●
15	●		●	●	●	●	●	●	●		●		●	●	●	
16	●		●	●		●	●	●	●				●	●	●	
17	●	●		●	●								●		●	
a	●			●	●										●	
b	●			●	●										●	
18	●		●		●					●			●		●	
a	*		500				500			*			250		*	
b				●	●								●		●	
19	●		●	●					●		●		●		●	●
a			40						40							60

Program Categories are Listed in Bold

Activities Under Those Programs are Indented

● Indicates an affirmative answer

* Refer to State Section

WILLIAM J. CALLAN, PH.D., DIRECTOR   205/260-3400
Bureau of Clinical Laboratories   FAX: 205/244-5083
8140 University Drive
Montgomery 36130-3017

Laboratories (Medical), Laboratories (Environmental)

Responsible for overall laboratory analysis.

NAJMUL CHOWDHURY, M.D., EPIDEMIOLOGIST   205/242-5131
Epidemiology   FAX: 205/288-5021
Department of Public Health
434 Monroe Street
Montgomery 36130-3017

Surveillance

Surveillance of elevated blood lead levels in children and adults.

SALVADOR GRAY, ENVIRONMENTAL ENGINEER   205/242-5007
Bureau of Environmental Services   FAX: 205/242-5000
Department of Public Health
434 Monroe Street
Montgomery 36117

Abatement/Standards and Enforcement, Environmental (General), Grant(s) Recipient, Inspections, Training/Certification/Accreditation

Provides environmental lead testing and consulting services. Performs lead-based paint testing, lead dust sampling, and soil sampling and provides lead abatement and prevention consultation for state agencies, public buildings, commercial buildings, and individual residences.

DONNA HANES, R.N., M.P.H., DIRECTOR   **205/242-5760**
Childhood Lead Poisoning Prevention Project   **FAX: 205/269-4865**
Division of Child Health
Bureau of Family Health Services
434 Monroe Street
Montgomery 36130-3017

Overall Lead Contact, Grant(s) Recipient, Public Outreach, Screening

Screening children as mandated by Medicaid; offer same services
to children with elevated blood lead levels; offer environmental
assessment if lead is found; contacts local housing authority if
publicly-owned; provides guidance.

State has statewide screening of all children ages 6 months to 6
years old; reportable at 15 µg/dL; above 20 µg/dL requires further
medical and environmental follow-up.

MELVIN HARAMAN, DIRECTOR   **205/242-5007**
Bureau of Environmental Services   **FAX: 205/242-5000**
434 Monroe Street, Rm 381
Montgomery 36130-1701

Abatement/Standards and Enforcement, Surveillance

Responsible for abatement programs and environmental
follow-up.

BARBARA HARRELL, M.P.A., ADMINISTRATOR   **205/242-5131**
Grant Project Director   **FAX: 205/288-5021**
Epidemiology
Department of Public Health
434 Monroe Street
Montgomery 36130-3017

Grant(s) Recipient, Surveillance

> Lead poisoning is reportable at 15 µg/dL or greater. Surveillance
> of elevated blood lead levels in children and adults.

ANIC LOPEZ, R.N., B.S.N., COORDINATOR   **205/242-5766**
Childhood Lead Poisoning Prevention Project   **FAX: 205/269-4865**
Division of Child Health Services
Bureau of Family Health Services
434 Monroe Street
Montgomery 36130-3017

Public Outreach

> Coordinator of CDC childhood lead poisoning prevention project
> grant.

WADE PITCHFORD, DIRECTOR   **205/242-5007**
Division of Environmental Program Management   **FAX: 205/242-5000**
Department of Public Health
434 Monroe Street
Montgomery 36130-3017

Abatement/Standards and Enforcement, Inspections, Soils,
Training/Certification/Accreditation

> Responsible for abatement programs and environmental
> follow-up.

PETE PRESTON, CHIEF   205/260-3494
Clinical Services   FAX: 205/244-5083
Bureau of Clinical Laboratories
8140 University Drive
Montgomery 36130-3017

Laboratories (Medical), Laboratories (Environmental)

Coordinates blood lead and environmental lead analysis.

JOE POWER, CHIEF   205/271-7773
Drinking Water Branch
Department of Environmental Management
1751 Congressman W.L. Dickenson Drive
Montgomery 36130

LCCA, Disposal (RCRA), NDWRL, Public Outreach, Soils

Responsible for the detection of lead in drinking water and soil,
and for disposal of lead wastes.

DAVID SHERROD, SUPERVISOR   205/260-3494
Lead Section   FAX: 205/260-5083
Bureau of Clinical Labs
8140 University Drive
Montgomery 36130-3017

Laboratories (Medical), Laboratories (Environmental)

Responsible for blood lead and environmental lead analyses.

JOHN SIKES, M.P.H., ASSISTANT DIRECTOR　　　205/348-4666
Safe State, Environmental Programs　　　**FAX: 205/348-9286**
University of Alabama
P.O. Box 870388
Tuscaloosa 35487-0388

Training/Certification/Accreditation

Responsible for the state's environmental compliance and for
training of lead abatement professionals.

NORMA VANCE, ACTING DIVISION DIRECTOR　　　205/260-3499
Microbiology Division　　　**FAX: 205/244-5083**
Bureau of Clinical Laboratories
8140 University Drive
Montgomery 36130-3017

Laboratories (Medical), Laboratories (Environmental)

Responsible for technical and scientific supervision of blood lead
and environmental analyses. The Bureau of Clinical Laboratories
provides screening and confirmatory testing for blood lead levels
of blood specimens, environmental samples of paint chips, soil,
and dust in order to confirm sources of lead poisoning.

CHARLES WOERNLE, M.D., M.P.H.　　　205/242-5131
Assistant State Health Officer　　　**FAX: 205/288-5021**
Disease Control and Prevention
Department of Public Health
434 Monroe Street
Montgomery 36130-0001

*Overall Lead Contact, Medical Contact, Occupational Safety and Health, Grant
Recipient*

Directs the entire epidemiological program, including the lead
program. The state requires reporting if the blood lead level in a
worker is 15 µg/dL or greater.

RICHARD CORMACK, MANAGER
Contaminated Sites Program
Spill Prevention and Planning
Department of Environmental Conservation
410 Willoughby Avenue, Ste. 105
Juneau 99801-1795

907/465-5200
FAX: 907/465-5218

Soils

Responsible for detection of lead in soils.

DEENA J. HENKINS, CHIEF
Drinking Water and Waste Water Section
Environmental Quality
Department of Environmental Conservation
410 Willoughby Avenue, Ste. 105
Juneau 99801-1795

907/465-5300
FAX: 907/465-5274

Overall Lead Contact, NDWRL

Responsible for drinking water regulations for lead.

JOHN MIDDAUGH, M.D.
Health and Social Services Epidemiology
P.O. Box 240249
Anchorage 99524-0249

907/561-4406

Medical Contact

Medical consultant for state lead activities.

ERIC SHORTT, C.I.H., ASSISTANT CHIEF   **907/269-4940**
Compliance   **FAX: 907/269-4950**
Department of Labor
Labor Standards and Safety
3301 Eagle Street, Ste. 305
P.O. Box 107022
Anchorage 99510-7022

Abatement/Standards and Enforcement, Occupational Safety and Health

Supervises technical industrial hygiene issues and is a certified industrial hygienist. Enforces state and federal OSHA standards for lead.

PATRICIA ADLER, MANAGER 602/542-6108
Division of State Laboratories FAX: 602/542-1169
Office of Environmental and Analytical Chemistry
Department of Health Services
1520 West Adams Street
Phoenix 85007-2605

Laboratories (Environmental), Laboratories (Medical)

Administers all environmental and public health chemistry
services, including blood lead and environmental lead analyses.

LESLIE BOYER, M.D., ASSOCIATE MEDICAL DIRECTOR 602/626-6229
Poison and Drug Information Center FAX: 602/626-2720
11501 North Campbell Avenue, Room 1156
Tucson 85724

Medical Contact

Medical consultant for state's lead programs.

BILL DePAUL, ACTING MANAGER 602/207-4104
Hazardous Waste Compliance Unit
Department of Environmental Quality
3033 North Central Avenue
Phoenix 85012

Disposal (RCRA)

Responsible for disposal of lead-based wastes.

CECILE FOWLER, EPIDEMIOLOGIST   **602/230-5862**
Office of Risk Assessment and Investigation   **FAX: 602/230-5817**
Department of Health Services
3008 North Third Street, Ste. 101
Phoenix 85012

Screening, Inspections, Surveillance

Responsible for screening and surveillance activities.

MICHAEL GOLDWATER, DIRECTOR   **602/542-1525**
Registrar of Contractors   **FAX: 602/542-1599**
800 West Washington, 6th floor
Phoenix 85007-2934

Abatement/Standards and Enforcement

No abatement standards or certification requirements at present.

MICHAEL KLEMINSKI   **602/207-4641**
Drinking Water Compliance Unit
Department of Environmental Quality
3033 North Central Avenue
Phoenix 85012

NDWRL, LCCA

Responsible for the detection of lead in drinking water.

FERNANDO MENDIETA, SUPERVISOR **602/542-1654**
Industrial Hygiene Compliance **FAX: 602/542-1614**
Division of Occupational Safety and Health
800 West Washington
P.O. Box 19070
Phoenix 85007-2922

Occupational Safety and Health

Requires employers to determine workplace exposures to lead,
and to reduce them if permissible limits are exceeded. Inspections
may be conducted in response to employee complaints, referrals
from regulatory agencies or physicians when overexposures are
suspected, or on a routine basis to determine compliance with
standards.

DALE OHNMEISS, UNIT MANAGER **602/207-4648**
Drinking Water Compliance **FAX: 602/207-4634**
Office of Water Quality
Department of Environmental Quality
3033 North Central
Phoenix 85012

LCCA, NDWRL, Public Outreach

Responsible for regulations concerning lead in drinking water,
provides guidance and outreach for state on environmental lead
poisoning.

NORMAN J. PETERSEN, CHIEF
Office of Risk Assessment and Investigation
Department of Health Services
3008 North Third Street
Phoenix 85012-3021

602/230-5858
FAX: 602/230-5817

Overall Lead Contact, Surveillance, Inspections

Provides lead poisoning education to public health personnel and health care providers.

JOE SOLTIS, MANAGER
Inorganics Section
Division of State Laboratories
Department of Health Services
1520 West Adams
Phoenix 85007-2605

602/542-6108
FAX: 602/542-1169

Laboratories (Medical), Laboratories (Environmental)

Responsible for blood lead and environmental lead analyses.

KEN FREE, HEALTH HAZARDS INVESTIGATOR   **501/661-2534**
Division of Sanitarian Services   **FAX: 501/661-2468**
Department of Health
4815 West Markham, Slot 46
Little Rock 72205-3867

Inspections, Public Housing, Public Outreach

Responsible for all health department environmental inspections
and surveillance, does some public housing inspections for HUD.

ROBERT HORN, DIRECTOR   **501/661-2191**
Department of Health   **FAX: 501/661-2310**
Public Health Laboratories
4815 West Markham, Slot 47
Little Rock 72205-3867

Laboratories (Medical), Laboratories (Environmental)

Responsible for analysis of blood lead samples and analysis of
lead in potable water.

PATSY LEWIS, BLOOD LEAD SCREENING COORDINATOR   **501/661-2592**
Division of Child and Adolescent Health   **FAX: 501/661-2055**
Department of Health
4815 West Markham, Slot 17
Little Rock 72205-3867

Overall Lead Contact, Screening

Responsible for follow-up of screening performed through the
health department; not responsible to private medical providers.

HAROLD R. SEIFERT, P.E., DIRECTOR
Engineering Division
Department of Health
4815 West Markham Street
Little Rock 72205-3867

501/661-2623
FAX: 501/661-2032

LCCA, NDWRL, Environmental (General), Public Outreach

Enforces lead standards for Safe Drinking Water Act.

BOB WEST, M.D., PEDIATRIC MEDICAL CONSULTANT
Division of Child and Adolescent Health
Department of Health
4815 West Markham, Slot 17
Little Rock 72205-3867

501/661-2757
FAX: 501/661-2055

Medical Contact

Responsible for case management of children identified with elevated blood lead levels.

FORTINO MIKE CARDENAS   **916/323-3014**
Construction Program Manager   **FAX: 916/323-4514**
Division of Community Affairs
Construction/Close-out Sub Unit
Department of Housing and Community Development
1800 3rd Street
Sacramento 95814-6414

Public Housing

> Responsible for detecting lead in state-owned, seasonal farm
> worker housing centers on any publicly funded residences.
> Monitors construction and/or rehabilitation activities of
> developments financed or otherwise assisted through funding
> from the department.

JENNIFER FLATTERY, ACTING CHIEF   **510/450-2426**
Surveillance Section   **FAX: 510/450-2442**
Childhood Lead Poisoning Prevention
Department of Health Services
5801 Christie Avenue, 6th floor
Emeryville 94608-2008

Screening, Surveillance

> Responsible for monitoring, screening, and coordinating follow-
> up through the state's childhood lead poisoning response and
> surveillance system.

PETER FLESSEL, PH.D., ENVIRONMENTAL BIOCHEMIST   **510/540-2475**
Air and Industrial Hygiene Laboratory   **FAX: 510/540-3022**
2151 Berkeley Way
Berkeley 94704-1011

Laboratories (Medical), Laboratories (Environmental)

> Provides blood lead and environmental sample lead analyses to
> support the Childhood Lead Poisoning Prevention Program.
> Provides reference laboratory services and quality assurance
> support in addition to routine testing.

REBECCA GAMBATESE, RESEARCH SCIENTIST   **510/450-2430**
Childhood Lead Poisoning Prevention   **FAX: 510/450-2442**
Department of Health Services
5801 Christie Avenue, 6th floor
Emeryville 94608

Surveillance

> Provides maintenance and expansion of the state's childhood lead
> poisoning response and surveillance system.

MARIDEE GREGORY, M.D., CHIEF   **916/654-0832**
Children's Medical Services   **FAX: 916/657-0796**
Department of Health Services
714 P Street, Room 323
Sacramento 95814-6414

Medical Contact, Screening

> Responsible for the Child Health and Disability Prevention
> (CHDP/EPSDT) program, which screens Medi-Cal and low
> income infants/children for lead poisoning, and the California
> Childrens Services (CCS) program, which provides diagnosis and
> treatment services to lead-burdened children.

LYNN GOLDMAN, M.D., M.P.H., CHIEF
Division of Environmental
and Occupational Disease Control
Department of Health Services
5801 Christie Avenue, 6th floor
Emeryville 94608-2008

510/450-2408
FAX: 510/450-2442

Medical Contact

Responsible for several epidemiological programs, including childhood lead poisoning prevention.

ANNE GORDON, M.P.H., HEALTH EDUCATOR
Childhood Lead Poisoning Prevention
Department of Health Services
5801 Christie Avenue, 6th floor
Emeryville 94608-2008

510/450-2433
FAX: 510/450-2442

Public Outreach

Coordinates education and outreach activities; develops written materials for the public and health professionals; coordinates training to local health departments.

GUIRGUIS GUIRGUIS, PH.D.
Public Health Chemist (Supervisory)
Department of Health Services, AIHL
2151 Berkeley Way
Berkeley 94704

510/540-2829
FAX: 510/540-3022

Laboratories (Medical), Laboratories (Environmental)

Responsible for blood lead and environmental lead analyses.

DAVID HARRINGTON, M.P.H.   **510/540-2788**
Education and Training Consultant   **FAX: 510/540-3472**
Occupational Lead Poisoning Prevention Program
Department of Health Services
2151 Berkeley Way, Annex 11
Berkeley 94704

Public Outreach

> Coordinates education, training, and outreach for workers,
> employers, health professionals, and others interested in
> preventing work-related lead poisoning.

BARBARA MATERNA, PH.D., CIH   **510/540-3481**
Program Coordinator, Industrial Hygienist   **FAX: 510/540-3472**
Occupational Lead Poisoning Prevention Program
Department of Health Services
2151 Berkeley Way, Annex 11
Berkeley 94704

Surveillance

> Coordinates Occupational Lead Poisoning Prevention Program.
> Program provides surveillance, case follow-up, training and
> educational materials, technical assistance, and intervention
> projects. Target audiences: Workers in lead using industries, those
> at risk from take-home lead exposure, employers, trade
> associations, health professionals, and others interested in
> preventing work-related lead poisoning.

ALEXIS MILEA   510/540-2177
Office of Drinking Water
Department of Health Services
2151 Berkeley Way, Room 113
Berkeley 94704

LCCA, NDWRL

> Responsible for regulations concerning lead in drinking water.

MARK NICAS, RESEARCH SCIENTIST   510/450-2415
Childhood Lead Poisoning Prevention   **FAX: 510/450-2442**
Department of Health Services
5801 Christie Avenue, 6th floor
Emeryville 94608-2008

Abatement/Standards and Enforcement , Grant Recipient

> Responsible for state's abatement policies and standards; received
> HUD grant.

ANA MARIA OSORIO, M.D., ACTING CHIEF   510/540-2175
Occupational Health Branch   **FAX: 510/540-3472**
Department of Health Services
2151 Berkeley Way, Annex 11
Berkeley 94704-1012

Overall Lead Contact, Medical Contact

> Responsible for various occupational health sections including the
> Occupational Lead Poisoning Prevention Program.

SUSAN PAYNE, MA, EPIDEMIOLOGIST
Occupational Lead Poisoning
Prevention Program
Department of Health Services
2151 Berkeley Way, Annex 11
Berkeley 94704

510/540-3125
FAX: 510/540-3472

Occupational Safety and Health, Surveillance

Coordinates the state's occupational lead surveillance program.

ALFREDO QUATTRONE, PH.D., D.A.B.T.
Food and Drug Branch
Department of Health Services
714 P Street
Sacramento 94234-7320

916/327-2577
FAX: 916/327-6326

Inspections, Surveillance

Regulatory toxicologic contact. Responsible for research and enforcement of levels of lead, mercury, and other hazardous substances in ethnic drugs, tableware, canned food, and other consumer products.

TED RAUH, ACTING DEPUTY DIRECTOR
Hazardous Waste Management Program
Department of Toxic Substances Control
400 P Street, 4th floor
P.O. Box 806
Sacramento 95812-0806

916/324-7193

Disposal (RCRA)

Responsible for disposal of toxics, including lead.

ROBERT SCHLAG, M.SC., ACTING CHIEF　　　**510/450-2413**
Childhood Lead Poisoning Prevention　　　　**FAX: 510/450-2442**
Department of Health Services
5801 Christie Avenue, 6th floor
Emeryville 94608-2008

Overall Lead Contact, Environmental (General),
Training/Certification/Accreditation

> Coordinates Childhood Lead Poisoning Prevention Program,
> which provides research, surveillance, technical assistance, and
> outreach. Program plans to provide financial assistance to local
> health departments through a fee to be imposed on industry.

TERI STOEBER, HEALTH EDUCATOR　　　**510/450-2434**
Childhood Lead Poisoning Prevention　　　**FAX: 510/450-2442**
Department of Health Services
5801 Christie Avenue., 6th floor
Emeryville 94608-2008

Public Outreach

> Coordinates outreach and education activities; develops
> educational materials, and provides training to local health
> departments.

KATHLEEN VORK, RESEARCH SCIENTIST　　　**510/450-2417**
Childhood Lead Poisoning Prevention　　　　**FAX: 510/450-2442**
Department of Health Services
5801 Christie Avenue, 6th floor
Emeryville 94608

Training/Certification/Accreditation

> Responsible for developing state's accreditations and standards.

JERRY WESOLOWSKI, PH.D., CHIEF
Air and Industrial Hygiene Lab
Department of Health Services
2151 Berkeley Way
Berkeley 94704-1011

510/540-2476
FAX: 510/540-3022

Laboratories (Medical), Environmental

Responsible for blood lead and environmental lead analyses to
support lead poisoning prevention programs.

GREG AKINS, PUBLIC HEALTH ENGINEER　　　　　**303/692-3548**
Water Quality Control　　　　　　　　　　**FAX: 303/782-0390**
Drinking Water Program
Department of Health
4300 Cherry Creek Drive South
Denver 80222-1530

NDWRL, Public Outreach

> Responsible for lead and copper regulations in plumbing, doing outreach to every plumber in the state to determine problem.

GLENN BODNAR, P.E., ENGINEERING UNIT LEADER　　**303/692-3548**
Drinking Water Section　　　　　　　　　**FAX: 303/782-0390**
Water Quality Control
Department of Health
4300 Cherry Creek Drive South
Denver 80222-1530

Environmental (General), NDWRL

> Responsible for several programs, including lead in drinking water.

MICHELE BOLYARD, ENVIRONMENTAL SCIENTIST　　**303/692-3548**
Water Quality Control Division　　　　　　**FAX: 303/782-0390**
Department of Health
4300 Cherry Creek Drive South
Denver 80222-1530

NDWRL

> Responsible for lead and copper regulations.

AMY JOHNSON   **303/692-2700**
Disease Control and Environmental Epidemiology   **FAX: 303/782-0188**
Department of Health
4300 Cherry Creek Drive South
Denver 80222-1530

Public Outreach, Surveillance

> Coordinates childhood lead poisoning surveillance activities. For
> all children younger than 18 years of age, blood lead levels are
> reportable at or above 10 µg/dL.

JANE BROWN MCCAMMON, DIRECTOR   **303/692-2639**
Occupational Epidemiology   **FAX: 303/329-3102**
Department of Health - DCEED
4300 Cherry Creek Drive South
Denver 80222-1530

Occupational Safety and Health, Surveillance

> Coordinates occupational lead activities. Lead poisoning in adults
> is reportable if blood lead levels are over 25 µg/dL.

MIKE WILSON, SECTION CHIEF   **303/692-2646**
Environmental Toxicology   **FAX: 303/329-3102**
Department of Health
4300 Cherry Creek Drive South
Denver 80222

Overall Lead Contact

> Responsible for state's environmental lead program, no active
> program at present.

CAROLYN JEAN DUPUY   **203/566-8167**
Occupational Health Program   **FAX: 203/566-1400**
Environmental Epidemiology and Occupational Health
Department of Health Services
150 Washington Street
Hartford 06106-4405

Occupational Safety and Health , Grant(s) Recipient, Screening, Surveillance

Coordinates adult blood lead surveillance program.

JANET KAPISH, M.P.H., DIRECTOR   **203/566-3701**
Environmental Chemistry Division
Bureau of Laboratories
Department of Health Services
10 Clinton Street
Hartford 06106

Laboratories (Environmental)

Oversight of analysis of soil, dust, and water for lead.

ROBERT RIVARD, SANITARY ENGINEER   **203/566-1253**
Department of Health   **FAX: 203/566-1710**
Water Supply Section
150 Washington Street
Hartford 06106-4405

Environmental (General), NDWRL

Responsible for regulations concerning lead in drinking water.

RONALD SKOMRO   **203/566-5808**
Supervising Environmental Sanitarian   **FAX: 203/566-2923**
Environmental Health
Department of Health Services
150 Washington Street
Hartford 06106-4405

Environmental (General), Inspections, Public Outreach,
Training/Certification/Accreditation

> Provides guidance to local health agencies on the implementation
> of the state's lead regulation. State requires approval for lead-
> training providers; will be establishing a lead inspector position
> and an abatement contractor certification program.

EARL THOMPSON, DIRECTOR   **203/566-3896**
Laboratory Standards/Clinical Chemistry   **FAX: 203/566-7813**
Department of Health Services
150 Washington Street
Hartford 06106-4405

Occupational Safety and Health, Grant(s) Recipient, Screening

> Coordinates occupational disease surveillance and intervention.

NARDA TOLENTINO, LEAD PROGRAM COORDINATOR   **203/566-5808**
Environmental Health Division   **FAX: 203/566-2923**
Department of Health Services
150 Washington Street
Hartford 06106-4405

Overall Lead Contact, Financing Projects, Grant(s) Recipient,
Abatement/Standards and Enforcement, Training/Certification/Accreditation,
Surveillance, Public Outreach

> The Lead Poisoning Prevention Program has responsibility for developing lead poisoning prevention policy; surveillance and tracking of all children with elevated blood lead levels; development and implementation of lead poisoning prevention programs and control of regulations; and providing financial assistance to local health departments for lead screening, education, and environmental management.

MARIHELEN BARRETT, R.N., M.S.N., DIRECTOR   **302/739-4735**
Children's Health Services   **FAX: 302/739-6617**
Division of Public Health
Maternal and Child Health
P.O. Box 637
Dover 19903

Financing Projects, Grant(s) Recipient, Medical Contact

Director of agency responsible for lead program.

EDWARD HALLOCK, PROGRAM MANAGER   **302/739-5410**
Public Water Systems Supervision Program   **FAX: 302/739-6617**
Division of Public Health
Health Systems Protection
P.O. Box 637
Dover 19903

NDWRL, LCCA

Responsible for detecting lead in drinking water.

JOHN A. HUGHES, DIRECTOR   **302/739-4411**
Division of Soil and Water Conservation
Department of Natural Resources
 and Environmental Control
89 Kings Highway
Dover 19901

Soils

Responsible for detecting lead in soil.

SATHYAVATHI LINGARAJU, DIRECTOR　　　　　　　302/739-4785
Maternal and Child Health Services　　　　　　**FAX: 302/739-6617**
Division of Public Health
P.O. Box 637
Dover 19903

Overall Lead Contact, Financing Projects, Medical Contact

    Coordinates private and public health agencies regarding
childhood health programs, including lead poisoning.

LISA MARENCIN, ASSISTANT　　　　　　　　302/739-4735
Children's Health Services　　　　　　　**FAX: 302/739-6617**
Maternal and Child Health
Division of Public Health
P.O. Box 637
Dover 19903

Grant(s) Recipient, Surveillance, Public Outreach

    Primary responsibility for statewide development and
implementation of childhood lead poisoning prevention efforts.
Management of financial resources from federal grants for CLPPP
services (CDC and MCH block grant).

NANCY MARKER　　　　　　　　　　　302/739-3689
Division of Air and Waste Management
Department of Natural Resources
 and Environmental Control
89 Kings Highway
Dover 19901

Disposal (RCRA)

    Responsible for hazardous waste disposal, including lead.

MARY MCKENZIE   **302/739-4411**
Division of Air and Waste Management
Department of Natural Resources
 and Environmental Control
89 Kings Highway
Dover 19901

Disposal (RCRA)

Responsible for hazardous waste disposal including lead.

CAROL PEARSON, R.N., B.S.N., TEAM LEADER   **302/995-8673**
Disease Prevention   **FAX: 302/995-8689**
Northern Health Service
Division of Public Health
3000 Newport Gap Pike, Bissell Campus Building C
Wilmington 19808

Medical Contact, Screening, Surveillance

Medical consultant for state's lead activities.

PAUL PUSEY, HEALTH PROGRAM COORDINATOR   **303/995-8693**
Division of Public Health   **FAX: 303/995-8689**
Childhood Lead Poisoning Prevention
3000 Newport Gap Pike
Bissell Hospital, Building C
Wilmington 19808

Inspections, Screening, Surveillance, Public Outreach

Coordinates childhood lead poisoning prevention activities within
the Division of Public Health; works with private health care
providers to ensure pediatric and/or environmental follow-up of
children identified with elevated blood lead levels; works with
local communities on lead poisoning prevention. Lead poisoning
is reportable above 25 µg/dL.

RICHARD STEIMAN, DEPUTY DIRECTOR   302/739-6603
Client Services and Health System Protection   **FAX: 302/739-6617**
Division of Public Health
P.O. Box 637
Dover 19903

*Abatement/Standards and Enforcement, Training/Certification/Accreditation,
Grant(s) Recipient, Environmental (General), NDWRL, LCCA*

> Responsible for implementing the federal drinking water
> standards.

MAHADEO VERMA, M.D., DIRECTOR   302/653-2870
Public Health Laboratory
30 Sunnyside Road
P.O. Box 1047
Smyrna 19977-1047

Laboratories (Medical)

> Responsible for blood lead sample analysis.

BARBARA WARD, SENIOR PUBLIC HEALTH EDUCATOR   302/995-8693
Childhood Lead Poisoning Prevention   **FAX: 302/995-8689**
Division of Public Health
Bissell Hospital, Building C
Wilmington 19808

Public Outreach

> Provides outreach on lead poisoning issues.

STEPHEN ARMS, CHEMIST ADMINISTRATOR　　　　904/359-6108
Office of Laboratory Services　　　　　　　　　FAX: 904/359-6015
Health and Rehabilitative Services
1217 Pearl Street
Jacksonville 32202

Environmental (General)

> The HRS Office of Laboratory Services Environmental Chemistry
> Program provides analytical support for County Public Health
> Units and other state agencies conducting investigations regarding
> lead poisoning prevention or remediation.

ANNE BOONE, ARNP, NURSE CONSULTANT, MEDICAID　　904/488-9228
Health and Rehabilitative Services　　　　　　　FAX: 904/488-2520
1317 Winewood Boulevard., Building 6, Ste. 280 B
Tallahassee 32399-0700

Screening

> EPSDT coordinator for the state; works with the director of
> Toxicology and Hazardous Assessment on publicizing problems
> of lead poisoning to Medicaid recipients.

MICHAEL CUPOLI, M.D., ASSISTANT SECRETARY,　　　904/487-2690
Children's Medical Services　　　　　　　　　　FAX: 904/488-3813
Health and Rehabilitative Services
1317 Winewood Boulevard., Building 5, Rm 129
Tallahassee 32399-0700

Medical Contact

> Oversees lead program for Children's Medical Services in
> collaboration with the health program.

RICHARD HOPKINS, M.D., M.S.P.H.　　　　　　**904/487-2542**
State Epidemiologist　　　　　　　　　　**FAX: 904/922-9299**
Health and Rehabilitative Services
1317 Winewood Boulevard., Building 2, Rm 245
Tallahassee 32399-0700

Surveillance

> Responsible for state's surveillance activities for epidemiological
> purposes.

ROGER INMAN, PH.D., DIRECTOR　　　　　　**904/488-3385**
Toxicology and Hazardous Assessment　　　**FAX: 904/488-2740**
Health and Rehabilitative Services
1317 Winewood Boulevard
Tallahassee 32399-0700

Overall Lead Contact

> Oversees lead program; responsible for initiation of pilot
> programs to test children for elevated blood level and follow-up to
> identify sources of exposure.

DWAYNE MAYS, CHEMIST III　　　　　　**904/359-6459**
Supervisor for Lead Laboratories　　　　**FAX: 904/359-6015**
Office of Laboratory Services
1217 Pearl Street
Jacksonville 32202-3926

Laboratories (Medical)

> Responsible for blood lead analysis.

VICKIE PRYOR, R.N., M.P.H., NURSING CONSULTANT   **904/488-2834**
Family Health Services   **FAX: 904/488-2341**
Health and Rehabilitative Services
1317 Winewood Boulevard
Tallahassee 32399-0700

Screening

> Responsible for establishing screening protocols and providing
> guidance and technical assistance to Health and Rehabilitative
> Services' County Public Health Units regarding prevention,
> detection, and case management of lead-poisoned children.

CHEMIST III (VACANT)   **904/359-6121**
Office of Laboratory Services   **FAX: 904/826-6015**
Health and Rehabilitative Services
1217 Pearl Street
Jacksonville 32202

Laboratories (Environmental)

> Responsible for environmental lead analysis.

SHARON WATKINS, ACTING CHIEF   **904/488-3370**
Environmental Epidemiology   **FAX: 904/922-6969**
1317 Winewood Boulevard
Tallahassee 32399-0700

Surveillance

> Responsible for statewide surveillance, coordination, and analysis
> of elevated childhood blood lead results.

HSIAO-CHUNG CHARLES WU, ENGINEER IV   **904/487-1762**
Drinking Water Section   **FAX: 904/487-3618**
Bureau of Drinking Water and Groundwater Resources
2600 Blair Stone Road, Rm 257 C
Tallahassee 32399-2400

LCCA, NDWRL

Implementation of lead and copper regulations according to the Safe Drinking Water Act.

MARION BROWN, MANAGER   **404/894-6644**
Environmental Health Program   **FAX: 404/894-7799**
Department of Human Resources
Environmental Health
878 Peachtree Street, N.E., Rm 100
Atlanta 30309

Overall Lead Contact, Financing Projects,

> Coordinates state's activity, mostly promoting and financing
> screening in Augusta and Savannah. State will investigate if
> elevated blood levels are detected, or if high concentrations of lead
> are found in environmental sources. Very minimal lead poisoning
> prevention activity at state level.

CHARLES REEVES   **404/595-2525**
Schools, Safety, and Environmental Services
Department of Education
132 Railroad Street
Thompson 30824-1965

LCCA, Public Outreach

> Responsible for informing schools of LCCA and requirements
> under the act.

HAROLD REHEIS, DIRECTOR   **404/656-4713**
Environmental Protection Division   **FAX: 404/651-9425**
Department of Natural Resources
205 Butler Street, S.E., Ste. 1152
Atlanta 30334

Environmental (General), Disposal (RCRA)

> Responsible for environmental protection for the state; state's
> environmental lead activities are minimal, no specific program in
> place.

DAVID WORD, ASSISTANT DIRECTOR   **404/656-4713**
Environmental Protection Division   **FAX: 404/651-9425**
Department of Natural Resources
205 Butler Street, S.E., Ste. 1152
Atlanta 30334

Environmental (General), Disposal (RCRA), NDWRL

Responsible for detection of lead in drinking water and disposal of lead-based wastes.

LESLIE AU, TOXICOLOGIST   **808/586-4250**
Hazard Evaluation Office   **FAX: 808/586-4370**
Department of Health
P.O. Box 3378
Honolulu 96801

Inspections, Surveillance

> Responsible for detection of lead in paints; state collects blood
> samples but does not analyze them. Lead poisoning is a reportable
> disease.

BARBARA BROOKS, CONSULTING TOXICOLOGIST   **808/586-4254**
Office of Hazard Evaluations/Emergency Responses   **FAX: 808/586-4370**
Department of Health
500 Ala Moana Boulevard
5 Waterfront Plaza, #250
Honolulu 96813-4913

Overall Lead Contact, Environmental (General), Public Outreach

> Provides information to public regarding lead poisoning
> prevention; research into lead problems within the state.

PATRICIA HEU, M.D.   **808/733-9022**
Maternal and Child Health Branch
Department of Health
P.O. Box 3378
Honolulu 96801-3378

Overall Lead Contact, Grant(s) Recipient, Screening,

> Received CDC grant to screen children and determine level of risk
> in the state.

FRITZ DIXON, STATE EPIDEMIOLOGIST   208/334-5939
Division of Health
450 West State Street, 4th floor
Boise 83720-0001

Medical Contact, Public Outreach

> Responsible for outreach to state physicians regarding lead
> poisoning; lead poisoning is reportable at 10 µg/dL.

PATRICIA MCGAVRAN, PH.D.   208/334-6584
State Public Health Toxicologist   FAX: 208/334-6581
Office of Environmental Health
Division of Health
450 West State Street, 4th floor
Boise 83720-0001

Overall Lead Contact, Environmental (General), Medical Contact

> Responsible for coordination of state activities; most activities
> delegated to local levels.

STEPHEN WEST, ENVIRONMENTAL HEALTH MANAGER   208/334-6584
Department of Health and Welfare   FAX: 208/334-6581
Division of Health
450 West State Street
Boise 83720-0001

Overall Lead Contact, Grant(s) Recipient, Surveillance

> Idaho State Lead Registry—identification and follow-up of
> individuals with lead levels greater than 10 µg/dL. Health
> intervention and screening for children at risk for exposure
> (Superfund and proposed NPL sites).

G. Michael Brandt, M.P.H., Chief **217/782-5830**
Asbestos and Lead Abatement Program **FAX: 217/785-0253**
Department of Public Health
525 West Jefferson
Springfield 62761-0001

*Abatement/Standards and Enforcement, Grant(s) Recipient, Inspections,
LCCA, Soils, Training/Certification/Accreditation*

> Implements environmental portion of the state lead poisoning
> protection program. The abatement portion will follow HUD
> guidelines; beginning training programs.

David Carpenter, Chief **217/782-6562**
State Laboratories
Department of Public Health
825 North Rutledge
Springfield 62794

Laboratories (Medical)

> Responsible for blood lead analysis.

JONAH DEPPE, M.S., ADMINISTRATOR   **217/782-4927**
Childhood Lead Poisoning Prevention Program   **FAX: 217/782-4890**
Division of Family Health
Department of Public Health
535 West Jefferson Street
Springfield 62761-0001

Overall Lead Contact, Financing Projects, Grant(s) Recipient, Medical Contact, Public Outreach, Screening, Surveillance

> Coordinates services for lead poisoning prevention with state laboratory, Division of Environmental Health, and local health departments; elevated blood level above 10 µg/dL is reportable; state will investigate cases. Received grant from CDC to do outreach. Lead Poisoning Prevention Act requires screening for children 6 months to 6 years, and requires screening prior to admission to day care homes or centers, preschool, nursery school, or kindergarten. Reporting systems for elevated blood lead levels; licensing of inspectors, contractors, and workers; and an information clearinghouse (1-800/545-2200).

MELINDA LEHNHERR, ACTING MANAGER   **217/785-1873**
Occupational Diseases Registry   **FAX: 217/524-1770**
Epidemiologic Studies
Department of Health
605 West Jefferson
Springfield 62761

Overall Lead Contact, Grant(s) Recipient, Occupational Safety and Health, Surveillance

> The Adult Blood Lead Registry (ABLR) is a surveillance system without regulatory authority. However, ABLR shares data with other IDPH lead programs (Environmental Health, Family Health) and outside agencies (Federal OSHA, IL Department of Labor) who conduct the intervention activities. ABLR also participates in the National Lead Registry.

JOSEPH A. MCCORD, PROJECT DIRECTOR　　　　**312/793-4639**
CDC Grant　　　　　　　　　　　　　　　　　**FAX: 312/793-4666**
Department of Public Health
33 East Congress
Chicago 60605

Grant(s) Recipient

> Responsible for administration of CDC-funded state and
> community board CLPPP programs in state-targeted areas to
> identify children with lead poisoning through door-to-door
> outreach efforts.

TOM CRONAU, DIRECTOR
Consumer Health Labs
State Department of Health
1330 West Michigan Street
Indianapolis 46206-1964

317/633-0224
FAX: 317/633-0868

Laboratories (Medical), Laboratories (Environmental)

Responsible for analyzing blood lead levels; also will test paint chips, dust, and soil samples for lead content.

DAVID ELLSWORTH, M.ED., DIRECTOR
Childhood Lead Poisoning Prevention Program
Maternal and Child Health
State Department of Health
1330 West Michigan Street
Indianapolis 46206-1964

317/633-0827
317/633-0662
FAX: 317/633-0776

Overall Lead Contact, Financing Projects, Grant(s) Recipient, Public Outreach, Screening, Surveillance

Screening follow-up education (high lab capacity with APIS three regional locations); CDC grantee; 10 lead regions with partially funded coordination.

BOB HILTON, BRANCH CHIEF
Drinking Water Branch
Department of Environmental Management
105 South Meridian Street
Indianapolis 46225-1016

317/233-4240
FAX: 317/233-4165

LCCA, Disposal (RCRA), NDWRL

Responsible for regulations concerning lead in drinking water.

MICHAEL HOOVER, CHIEF OF ENVIRONMENTAL HEALTH   **317/633-0183**
Division of Sanitarian Engineering   **FAX: 317/633-0776**
State Department of Health
1330 West Michigan Street
Indianapolis 46206-2829

Environmental (General), Inspections, Public Housing

> Responsible for environmental follow-up when elevated blood
> levels have been detected.

DENNIS ALT, MANAGER 515/281-8998
Public Water Supply Program
Department of Natural Resources
Wallace Street Office Building
East 9th and Grand
Des Moines 50319

NDWRL

Responsible for regulations concerning lead in drinking water.

KENNETH CHOQUETTE 515/281-8220
Environmental Program Supervisor FAX: 515/242-6284
Division of Health Protection
Department of Public Health
Lucas State Office Building
321 East 12th Street
Des Moines 50319-0001

Overall Lead Contact

Coordinates lead activities for the state. State actively seeking funding to conduct screening for children; trying to develop abatement guidance document; doing public outreach to rural communities and other targeted areas. Finances certain local projects.

CHARLES DANIELSON, M.D., MEDICAL DIRECTOR 515/281-4912
Division of Family and Community Health FAX: 515/242-6384
Department of Health
Lucas Street Office Building
321 East 12th Street
Des Moines 50319-0001

Medical Contact

Medical consultant for the maternal and child health program.

LEE FRIELL, MANAGER   **515/281-5371**
University Hygienic Laboratory   **FAX: 515/243-1349**
Wallace State Office Building
East 9th and Grand
Des Moines 50319

Laboratories (Medical), Laboratories (Environmental)

Responsible for blood lead and environmental lead analyses.

RITA GERGELY, ENVIRONMENTAL SPECIALIST   **515/242-6340**
Division of Health Protection   **FAX: 515/242-6284**
Department of Public Health
Lucas Street Office Building
321 East 12th Street
Des Moines 50319-0001

Financing Projects, Grant(s) Recipient, Inspections, LCCA, Public Outreach, Screening, Surveillance, Training/Certification/Accreditation

Program manager for CDC grant. Oversees local projects and case management of lead poisoned children at the state level. The results of all blood lead testing for children must be reported to the Department of Public Health.

KAY GROTHER, M.C.H., NURSE CONSULTANT   **515/242-5159**
Family and Community Health   **FAX: 515/242-6384**
Department of Public Health
321 East 12th Street
Des Moines 50319-0001

Medical Contact

Coordinates the EPSDT screening program.

CHARLES HOOPER, ACTING LABOR SAFETY OFFICER　　　515/281-3606
Division of Labor
Occupational Safety and Health Bureau
1000 East Grand Avenue
Des Moines 50319

Occupational Safety and Health

Responsible for safety and health activities regarding lead.

SHIRLEY JONES, PROGRAM PLANNER　　　**515/281-7056**
Division of Health Protection　　　**FAX: 515/242-6284**
Department of Public Health
Lucas State Office Building
Des Moines 50319

Surveillance

Responsible for surveillance of adult blood lead. The results of all adult blood lead testing must be reported to the Department of Public Health.

ROGER CARLSON, PH.D., DIRECTOR　　　　　　　**913/296-1620**
Health and Environmental Laboratory　　　　　　**FAX: 913/296-1641**
Department of Health and Environment
Forbes Field, Building 740
Topeka 66620

Laboratories (Medical), Laboratories (Environmental)

Responsible for blood lead and environmental lead analyses.

RONALD HAMMERSCHMIDT, PH.D., DEPUTY DIRECTOR　　　**913/296-1535**
Division of Environment　　　　　　　　　　　　**FAX: 913/296-6247**
Department of Health and Environment
Forbes Field, Building 740
Topeka 66620

Environmental (General)

Responsible for environmental lead activities.

GARY MILLER, CHIEF　　　　　　　　　　　　　**913/296-1547**
Asbestos Control　　　　　　　　　　　　　　　**FAX: 913/296-6247**
Bureau of Air and Radiation
Department of Health and Environment
Forbes Field, Building 740
Topeka 66620

Abatement/Standards and Enforcement

Responsible for developing abatement standards.

STEPHEN PAIGE, M.P.A., DIRECTOR　　　　　　913/296-0189
Bureau of Environmental Health Services　　　　FAX: 913/296-0984
Department of Health and Environment
109 Southwest 9th Street, Ste. 604
Topeka 66612-1274

Overall Lead Contact, Financing Projects, Grant(s) Recipient, Screening

> The Department of Health and Environment is pursuing state
> funding to support screening and inspection activities of local
> health agencies.

ANDREW PELLETIER, M.D., ACTING STATE EPIDEMIOLOGIST 913/296-5586
Bureau of Disease Control　　　　　　　　　　　FAX: 913/296-4197
Department of Health and Environment
109 Southwest 9th Street, Ste. 605
Topeka 66612-1271

Medical Contact, Surveillance

> Medical consultant for state's lead activities.

DAVID F. WALDO, CHIEF　　　　　　　　　913/296-5503
Public Water Supply Section　　　　　　　　FAX: 913/296-6247
Department of Health and Environment
Forbes Field, Building 740
Topeka 66620

LCCA, NDWRL

> Responsible for regulations concerning lead in drinking water.

PAT BEELER, DISEASE SURVEILLANCE TECHNICIAN   **502/564-3418**
Division of Epidemiology   **FAX: 502/564-6533**
Department of Health Services
275 East Main Street
Frankfort 40621-0001

Surveillance

Coordinates lead reporting requirements.

CHANDRAKANT C. PATEL, M.D.   **502/629-8815**
601 South Floyd Street
Louisville 40202

Medical Contact

Provides medical supervision for the state's lead program.

ANN JOHNSON, LEAD PROGRAM COORDINATOR   **502/564-2154**
Maternal and Child Health   **FAX: 502/564-8389**
Cabinet for Human Resources
Department of Health Services
275 East Main Street
Frankfort 40621-0001

Overall Lead Contact, Grant(s) Recipient,

Screens children 6 months to 6 years of age statewide in all Well
Child Clinics. Currently reviewing a pilot project with a private
physician by use of a risk assessment. Analyzing data from an
additional pilot project to evaluate the use of a risk assessment in
identifying at-risk and lead-poisoned children.

THOMAS E. MAXSON, DIRECTOR　　　　502/564-4446
Division of Laboratory Services　　　　**FAX: 502/564-6533**
Department of Health Services
275 East Main Street
Frankfort 40621-0001

Laboratories (Environmental)

> State laboratory analyzes paint chips and does environmental analysis of lead.

PATRICIA SCHMIDT, NURSE CONSULTANT　　　502/564-2154
Division of Maternal and Child Health　　　**FAX: 502/564-8389**
Specialized Pediatrics
275 East Main Street
Frankfort 40621-0001

Laboratories (Medical), Grant(s) Recipient, Screening

> Three funded sites in Kentucky are Northern Kentucky District, Lexington-Fayette County Health Department, and Louisville Jefferson County Health Department. Children are screened in the WIC and Well Child and EPSDT programs. Louisville Jefferson County also does door-to-door screening for children living in high risk areas. All health departments screen children in Well Child and EPSDT. Northern Kentucky District screens children.

CECIL WEBB, JR., MANAGER　　　　502/564-4446
Chemistry Branch　　　　**FAX: 502/564-6533**
Cabinet for Human Resources
Department of Health Services
275 East Main Street
Frankfort 40621-0001

Laboratories (Environmental)

> Responsible for environmental lead analysis.

TERRY WESCOTT, MANAGER
Product Safety Branch
Division of Community Services
Department of Health Services
275 East Main Street
Frankfort 40621-0001

502/564-4537
FAX: 502/564-6533

Abatement/Standards and Enforcement, Environmental (General)

Responsible for enforcing state lead-based paint law.

SARAH WILDING, SUPERVISOR
Maternal and Child Health
Department for Health Services
275 East Main Street
Frankfort 40621-0001

502/564-2154
FAX: 502/564-8389

Overall Lead Contact, Grant(s) Recipient, Public Outreach, Screening

Supervises the administration and implementation of the state's lead program. Prepares or approves applications and federal reports. Recommends program modifications and policy changes.

CHARLES ANDERSON, R.S.　　　　　　　504/568-8343
Sanitarian Program Manager　　　　　　FAX: 504/568-5119
Sanitarian Services
Office of Public Health
P.O. Box 60630, Room 210
New Orleans 70160-0630

Abatement/Standards and Enforcement, Inspections

Responsible for enforcing the abatement standards.

HENRY B. BRADFORD, PH.D., DIRECTOR OF LABORATORIES　504/568-7684
Office of Public Health　　　　　　　　FAX: 504/568-5393
Department of Health and Hospitals
P.O. Box 60630, 7th floor
New Orleans 70160-0630

Laboratories (Medical), Laboratories (Environmental)

Responsible for blood lead and environmental lead analyses.

EMILIO M. DE ZUBIZARRETA, M.T.(ASCP), M.S. HYG　504/568-7684
Laboratory Scientist Manager　　　　　FAX: 504/568-5393
Office of Public Health
Department of Health and Hospitals
P.O. Box 60630, 7th floor
New Orleans 70160-0630

Screening

Responsible for blood lead screening and confirmation.

EVE HARTZ FLOOD, R.N., M.P.H., NURSE CONSULTANT   **504/568-5070**
Genetic Disease and Lead Programs   **FAX: 504/568-2543**
Office of Public Health
P.O. Box 60630, Room 308
New Orleans 70160-0630

Overall Lead Contact, Screening, Surveillance

Coordinates state lead program; the program involves screening, environmental inspections, and follow-up. Most activity is at parish (county) level but funded by the state. No abatement program at present, but state Sanitary Code has developed guidelines. Lead poisoning is a reportable disease. Program screens all children coming into child health clinics (ages 1-6), those at high risk, and children living in same household as lead cases.

CHARLES MYERS, M.S.W., ADMINISTRATOR   **504/568-5070**
Genetic Disease and Lead Programs   **FAX: 504/568-2543**
Office of Public Health
P.O. Box 60630, Room 308
New Orleans 70160-0630

Overall Lead Contact, Screening

Director of agency responsible for lead program.

T. JAY RAY, DIRECTOR   **504/568-5101**
Environmental Health Services Division   **FAX: 504/568-7703**
Department of Health and Hospitals
P.O. Box 60630, Room 403
New Orleans 70160-0630

Environmental (General), LCCA, NDWRL

Responsible for detecting lead in drinking water; will do environmental inspections if high lead levels are discovered.

JEAN TAKENAKA, M.D., PEDIATRIC MEDICAL CONSULTANT   **504/568-5142**
Maternal and Child Health   **FAX: 504/568-8162**
Office of Public Health
P.O. Box 60630, Room 605
New Orleans 70160-0630

Medical Contact

> Provides medical consultation for the state screening program
> which screens children from ages 1 to 6 years who attend well-
> child clinics in the state health department. Surveillance of
> reported cases is also maintained.

FRANK DRAKE, MANAGER   **207/287-5680**
Drinking Water Program   **FAX: 207/287-4172**
Bureau of Health
State House Station 10
157 Capitol Street
Augusta 04333-0010

NDWRL, LCCA

Responsible for regulations concerning lead in drinking water.

EDNA JONES, DIRECTOR   **207/287-4311**
Childhood Lead Poisoning Prevention Program   **FAX: 207/287-4172**
State House Station 11
157 Capitol Street
Augusta 04333-0010

Overall Lead Contact, Financing Projects, Grant(s) Recipient, Medical Contact, Screening, Surveillance, Public Outreach, LCCA

Coordinates the state's lead program; main focus is on lead-based paint in residences. Screening is required for children attending well child clinics sponsored by state funds and as part of an EPSDT exam. Private medical providers are encouraged to incorporate screening into office routine for all children.

JEANNE THAYER, LAB TECHNICIAN   **207/287-2727**
Health and Environmental Testing Laboratory   **FAX: 207/626-5555**
Department of Human Services
221 State Street, Station 12
Augusta 04333-0001

Laboratories (Medical), Laboratories (Environmental)

Responsible for blood lead and environmental lead analyses.

STEVE ZAYSZLY, ENVIRONMENTAL HEALTH SPECIALIST   **207/287-4311**
Childhood Lead Poisoning Prevention Program   **FAX: 207/287-4172**
Bureau of Health
State House Station 11
157 Capitol Street
Augusta 04333-0010

Inspections, Abatement/Standards and Enforcement,
Training/Certification/Accreditation, Soils

Responsible for environmental investigations of areas after lead
contamination has been identified.

JULIAN CHISOLM, JR., M.D., DIRECTOR
Lead Poisoning Program
Kennedy Institute
707 North Broadway Street, Room 407
Baltimore 21213-3941

410/550-9035
FAX: 410/550-9344

Medical Contact

Medical consultant for the state's lead program.

ELLEN COE, R.N., M.P.H.
Office of Environmental Health Coordination
Department of the Environment
2500 Broening Highway
Baltimore 21224-6612

410/631-3852
FAX: 410/631-4112

Surveillance

Manages statewide adult lead registry, which requires laboratories to report elevated blood lead levels greater than 25 µg/dL.

BARBARA CONRAD, R.N., M.P.H., ADMINISTRATOR
Lead Coordination Program
Department of the Environment
2500 Broening Highway
Baltimore 21224-6612

410/631-3847
FAX: 410/631-4112

Overall Lead Contact

The Lead Paint Poisoning Commission has statutory mandate to "study and recommend means of implementing an equitable, effective and self-funded...compensation and prevention system." The Governor's Advisory Council on Lead Poisoning reviews issues of concern and promotes appropriate responses.

BEVERLY GAMMAGE, B.S.N., M.S., CHIEF   **410/631-3859**
Lead Poisoning Prevention Division   **FAX: 410/631-4112**
Department of the Environment
2500 Broening Highway
Baltimore 21224-6612

Screening, Surveillance, Grant(s) Recipient

> Responsible for screening program, manages childhood lead
> registry, provides nursing consulting. Screening is conducted
> through Healthy Kids (EPSDT) providers and local health
> departments.

MARILYN GALLAGHER, HEAD OF BLOOD LEAD LABORATORY 410/225-6086
Laboratory Administrations   **FAX: 410/333-5403**
State Health Department
201 West Preston
Baltimore 21201-2323

Laboratories (Medical)

> Responsible for blood lead analysis.

BOYD GROVE, SANITARIAN   **410/631-3716**
Water Supply Program   **FAX: 410/631-0456**
Department of the Environment
2500 Broening Highway
Baltimore 21224-6612

LCCA

> Responsible for detecting lead in drinking water.

SUSAN GUYAUX
Lead Compliance Division
Department of the Environment
2500 Broening Highway
Baltimore 21224-6612

410/631-3824
FAX: 410/631-4112

Abatement/Standards and Enforcement, Grant(s) Recipient, Inspections,
Environmental (General)

> Abatements are ordered by local health or housing agencies.
> Received grant from EPA.

ED HAMMERBERG, CHIEF
Federal Facilities Division
Department of the Environment
2500 Broening Highway
Baltimore 21224-6612

410/631-3343
FAX: 410/631-3321

Disposal (RCRA)

> Responsible for regulating disposal of hazardous waste, including
> lead.

POLLY HARRISON, M.D., DIRECTOR
Child Health Services
Department of Health and Mental Hygiene
201 West Preston Street
Baltimore 21201-2323

410/225-6749
FAX: 410/333-5995

Screening

> Administers Healthy Kids (EPSDT) program, which requires
> blood lead testing of enrolled children.

J. MEHSEN JOSEPH, PH.D., DIRECTOR   **410/225-6100**
Laboratories Administration   **FAX: 410/333-5403**
Department of Health and Mental Hygiene
201 West Preston Street
Baltimore 21201-2323

Laboratories (Medical), Laboratories (Environmental)

     Responsible for policies and procedures for laboratory analysis of lead.

BEVERLY LONG, PUBLIC HEALTH ENGINEER   **410/631-3706**
Water Supply Program   **FAX: 410/631-4894**
Department of the Environment
2500 Broening Highway
Baltimore 21224-6612

NDWRL

     Responsible for detecting lead in public drinking water.

VANCE MORRIS, DIRECTOR   **410/514-7565**
Special Loan Programs   **FAX: 410/987-4097**
Department of Housing and Community Development
100 Community Place
Crownsville 21032-2023

Financing Projects, Overall Lead Contact

     Responsible for residential lead abatement and housing rehabilitation program.

WILLIAM PALM, HEALTH EDUCATION SPECIALIST
Lead Poisoning Prevention
Department of the Environment
2500 Broening Highway
Baltimore 21224-6612

401/631-3859
FAX: 410/631-4112

Public Outreach, Training/Certification/Accreditation

Responsible for training; reviews and approves training programs
and worker training certification. Provides outreach to local
schools and communities. Legislation and regulations under
development to expand training and certification requirements.

MILTON H.F. SAUL, ASSISTANT COMMISSIONER
Occupational Safety and Health (MOSH)
501 Saint Paul Place
Baltimore 21202

410/333-4195
FAX: 410/333-1771

Occupational Safety and Health

Responsible for enforcing occupational lead standards and
providing consultative assistance and training to employers
regarding lead hazards.

DAVID SEVDALIAN, HEAD OF MULTIELEMENT LABS
Laboratory Administration
State Health Department
201 West Preston
Baltimore 21201-2323

410/225-6944
FAX: 410/333-5403

Laboratories (Environmental)

Responsible for environmental lead analysis.

PAUL ABOODY, DIRECTOR   617/969-7177
Occupational Hygiene   FAX: 617/727-4581
Department of Labor and Industries
1001 Watertown Street
West Newton 02165-2104

Laboratories (Medical), Laboratories (Environmental), Occupational Safety and Health

Responsible for lead activities within occupational settings.

JILL ANTONELLIS, HEALTH EDUCATOR   617/522-3700
Childhood Lead Poisoning Prevention Program
Department of Health
305 South Street
Jamaica Plain 02130

Public Outreach

Responsible for public outreach and education.

RICHARD BOHN, DIRECTOR   617/727-3250
Bureau of Housing Develop and Construction   FAX: 617/727-0082
Executive Office of Communities and Development
100 Cambridge Street, 17th floor
Boston 02202-0016

Public Housing

Coordinates lead activities for the state housing agency; responsible for lead abatement in public housing and the rental assistance program.

MARY JEAN BROWN, R.N., ASSISTANT DIRECTOR   **617/522-3700**
Childhood Lead Poisoning Prevention   **FAX: 617/522-3700**
Department of Health
305 South Street
Jamaica Plain 02130-4747

Grant(s) Recipient, Medical Contact, Screening, Surveillance

> Coordinates health department lead poisoning programs;
> responsible for screening, detecting blood lead levels, and drafting
> grants. Lead poisoning is a reportable disease.

YVETTE DePEIZA, PROGRAM MANAGER   **617/292-5857**
Department of Environmental Protection   **FAX: 617/556-1049**
Division of Water Supply
1 Winter Street
Boston 02130-4747

*Overall Lead Contact, Abatement/Standards and Enforcement, LCCA,
NDWRL*

> Responsibility for overseeing the implementation of the federal
> drinking water standards for lead and copper as well as the Lead
> Contamination Control Act. This includes providing training for
> public water suppliers, reviewing their monitoring data, their
> corrosion control plans, and their public information strategies.

LINDA DUBE, SENIOR INSPECTOR
Childhood Lead Poisoning Prevention
Department of Health
305 South Street
Jamaica Plain 02130

617/522-3700
FAX: 617/522-3700

Financing Projects, Inspections

> Responds to complaints about private inspection services; develops quality control initiatives to improve the quality of inspections. Works with state housing agency regarding financing projects.

GENE GRILLO, DIRECTOR
Industrial Safety
Department of Labor and Industries
100 Cambridge Street, 11th floor
Boston 02202-0001

617/727-3567
FAX: 617/727-8022

Abatement/Standards and Enforcement

> Responsible for enforcement of abatement standards.

PAUL HUNTER, ASSISTANT DIRECTOR
Childhood Lead Poisoning Prevention
Department of Health
305 South Street
Jamaica Plain 02130

617/522-3700
FAX: 617/522-3700

Abatement/Standards and Enforcement, Inspections, Training/Certification/Accreditation

> Responsible for the environmental portion of the state's lead program and for the training and accreditation of abatement professionals. Also responsible for state's OSHA responsibilities regarding lead.

CHARLES LARSON, ENVIRONMENTAL ENGINEER   **617/292-5927**
Department of Environmental Protection   **FAX: 617/556-1049**
Division of Water Supply
1 Winter Street
Boston 02108-4747

NDWRL

Responsible for regulations concerning lead in drinking water.

JULIANNE NASSIF, DIRECTOR   **617/522-3700**
Environmental Chemistry Laboratories   **FAX: 617/522-3700**
Department of Health
305 South Street
Jamaica Plain 02130

Laboratories (Medical), Laboratories (Environmental)

Responsible for blood lead and environmental lead analyses.

ROY PETRE, SENIOR PLANNER   **617/522-3700**
Childhood Lead Poisoning Prevention Program
Department of Public Health
305 South Street
Jamaica Plain 02130

Public Outreach, Environmental

Responsible for regulation development, policy analysis and
development, and legislative affairs. Handles environmental and
legal issues.

BRAD PRENNEY, DIRECTOR   617/522-3700
Childhood Lead Poisoning Prevention   **FAX: 617/522-3700**
Department of Health
305 South Street
Jamaica Plain 02130

Overall Lead Contact, Abatement/Standards and Enforcement, Financing Projects, Grant(s) Recipient

> Coordinates the state's lead initiative; oversees both the health and the environmental lead programs.

RICHARD RABIN, COORDINATOR   617/969-7177
Lead Registry   **FAX: 617/727-4581**
Department of Labor and Industries
Division of Occupational Hygiene
1001 Watertown Street
Newton 02165-2104

Grant(s) Recipient, Surveillance

> The state receives reports of blood lead levels in adults of 15 µg/dL or higher; performs interviews of adults with elevated blood lead levels (15 years or older); supplies education on lead for workers, employers, and physicians; performs workplace investigations and does data analysis of lead registry findings.

WILLIAM SIRULL, ENVIRONMENTAL ANALYST   617/292-5838
Compliance/Enforcement Branch   **FAX: 617/556-1049**
Division of Hazardous Waste
Department of Environmental Protection
1 Winter Street
Boston 02108-4747

Disposal (RCRA)

> Responsible for any lead disposal; lead is one of several toxins regulated.

MAUREEN TIVNAN, DIRECTOR   **617/727-1933**
Department of Labor and Industries
100 Cambridge Street, 11th floor
Boston 02202-0001

Training/Certification/Accreditation

Responsible for licensing of deleading (abatement) contractors.

LOUIS VISCO, EXECUTIVE SECRETARY   **617/727-9952**
Plumbing Board   **FAX: 617/727-2197**
Board of Registration
100 Cambridge Street, Room 1511
Boston 02202-0001

NDWRL, LCCA

Responsible for regulations concerning lead in drinking water.

JAMES BEDFORD, ENVIRONMENTAL HEALTH OMBUDSMAN   **517/335-9215**
Division of Health Risk Assessment   **FAX: 517/335-8560**
Department of Public Health
3423 North Logan
P.O. Box 30195
Lansing 48909

Environmental

Responsible for environmental component of state's lead activity.

ALETHIA CARR, COORDINATOR   **517/335-9263**
Childhood Lead Poisoning Prevention Program   **FAX: 517/335-9222**
Child and Adolescent Health
Department of Public Health
3423 North Logan
P.O. Box 30195
Lansing 48909

Overall Lead Contact, Financing Projects, Grant(s) Recipient, Public Outreach, Screening, Soils, Surveillance

Responsible for Childhood Lead Poisoning Prevention Program which includes screening intervention (both medical and environmental); professional and public education; tracking of all elevated levels in children 0-6 years of age.

JAMES K. CLELAND, CHIEF   **517/335-8326**
Division of Water Supply   **FAX: 517/335-8298**
Department of Public Health
3423 North Logan
P.O. Box 30195
Lansing 48909

Grant(s) Recipient, LCCA, NDWRL

Responsible for regulations concerning lead in drinking water.

GEORGE HOWARD, INDUSTRIAL HYGIENIST SUPERVISOR   **517/335-8246**
Occupational Health   **FAX: 517/335-8560**
Department of Public Health
3423 North Logan
P.O. Box 30095
Lansing 48909

Abatement/Standards and Enforcement

Responsible for abatement guidance for the state.

DOUGLAS KALINOWSKI, ACTING CHIEF   **517/335-8221**
Division of Occupational Health   **FAX: 517/335-8298**
Bureau of Environmental and Occupational Health
Department of Public Health
3423 North Logan
P.O. Box 30195
Lansing 48909

Occupational Safety and Health

Responsible for lead detection in occupational settings.

DOUG BENSON, LEAD COORDINATOR   **612/627-5017**
Department of Health   **FAX: 612/627-5479**
925 Delaware Street, S.E.
P.O. Box 59040
Minneapolis 55459-0040

Overall Lead Contact, Abatement/Standards and Enforcement, NDWRL,
Surveillance

> Responsible for development of state's rules and regulations
> regarding lead in paint, dust, and drinking water. Lead poisoning
> is a reportable disease.

PAULINE BOUCHARD, J.D., LABORATORY DIRECTOR   **612/623-5331**
Public Health Laboratory   **FAX: 612/623-5514**
Department of Health
717 Delaware Street, S.E.
Minneapolis 55440

Laboratories (Medical), Laboratories (Environmental)

> Responsible for blood lead and environmental lead analyses.

DEBORAH GRUNDMANIS   **612/627-5494**
Lead Program   **FAX: 612/627-5479**
Department of Health
925 Delaware Street, S.E.
P.O. Box 59040
Minneapolis 55459-0040

Training/Certification/Accreditation

> Responsible for any training or certification activities.

DIANNE KOCOUREK PLOETZ, HEALTH EDUCATOR　　　　**612/627-5018**
Lead Program　　　　　　　　　　　　　　　　　　**FAX: 612/627-5479**
Department of Health
925 Delaware Street, S.E.
P.O. Box 59040
Minneapolis 55459-0040

Public Outreach, Training/Certification/Accreditation

> Provides information to parents, educators, and health care
> providers and responds to calls from the public. Screening project
> in progress.

PLACIDA VENEGAS, J.D.　　　　　　　　　　　　**612/297-8370**
Senior Pollution Control Specialist　　　　　　　**FAX: 612/297-8676**
Pollution Control Agency
520 Lafayette Road
St. Paul 55155-3898

Overall Lead Contact, Environmental (General), Disposal (RCRA), Soils

> Responsible for the regulatory development of the state's lead
> waste disposal legislation, soil lead rules, soil lead standards, and
> abatement methods and other lead initiatives.

KRIS ZETTERLUND, PUBLIC HEALTH SANITARIAN　　**612/627-5013**
Lead Program　　　　　　　　　　　　　　　　　　**FAX: 612/627-5479**
Department of Health
925 Delaware Street, S.E.
P.O. Box 59040
Minneapolis 55459-0040

Inspections

> Responsible for residential inspections and enforcement, and
> technical support for local health agencies.

ERNEST GRIFFIN, DIVISION DIRECTOR　　　　　601/960-7463
Child Health Division　　　　　　　　　　FAX: 601/960-7448
Department of Health
P.O. Box 1700
Jackson 39215-1700

Overall Lead Contact, Public Outreach, Screening

Lead screening currently being done on a case-by-case basis on
children through local health department clinics who present
symptoms associated with elevated blood lead levels. The agency
is currently developing guidelines to address OBRA 1989
requirements for lead screening under the EPSDT program.

SAM MABRY, CHIEF　　　　　　　　　　601/961-5062
Office of Pollution Control　　　　　　　FAX: 601/961-5741
Hazardous Waste Division
P.O. Box 10385
Jackson 39289-0385

Disposal (RCRA), Soils

Responsible for all hazardous waste, including lead.

ERIC BLANK, DR. P.H., DIRECTOR
State Public Health Laboratory
Department of Health,
 Environmental Health and Epidemiology
307 West McCarty Street
Jefferson City 65101-1535

314/751-3334
FAX: 314/751-7219

Laboratories (Medical), Laboratories (Environmental)

The state public health laboratory conducts blood lead analysis
and environmental lead analysis in conjunction with state and
local health department lead poisoning prevention programs.

MICHAEL CARTER, LEAD PROGRAM COORDINATOR
Department of Health
Bureau of Environmental Epidemiology
1730 East Elm Street
P.O. Box 570
Jefferson City 65102

314/751-6080
FAX: 314/751-6010

Overall Lead Contact

Responsible for development of CDC proposal and overall
coordination of lead prevention and control activities.

JERRY L. LANE, DIRECTOR
Public Drinking Water Program
Environmental Quality Division
205 Jefferson Street
Jefferson City 65102

314/751-5331
FAX: 314/751-3110

NDWRL, LCCA, Public Outreach

Responsible for lead detection in drinking water.

DARYL ROBERTS, BUREAU CHIEF   314/751-6102
Department of Environmental Epidemiology   FAX: 314/751-6010
Department of Health
1730 Elm Street
P.O. Box 570
Jefferson City 65102-0570

Overall Lead Contact, Abatement/Standards and Enforcement, Grant(s) Recipient, Public Outreach, LCCA, Surveillance

State screening program is possible if budget item is approved. The state is seeking grants from CDC for screening and public outreach. Legislation for licensing of abatement workers and inspectors is pending. Provides information to schools and day care centers. Lead poisoning is a reportable disease as of April 1, 1993.

WILLIAM R. SCHMIDT, M.P.H. PA-C, DIRECTOR   314/751-6080
Division of Environmental Health and Epidemiology **FAX: 314/751-6010**
Department of Health
1730 Elm Street
P.O. Box 570
Jefferson City 65102-0570

Public Outreach

Responsible for administration of communicable disease and environmental programs, including lead poisoning prevention and control. Legislative contact on lead issues.

JAMES WILLIAMS, PH.D., DIRECTOR　　　　　　　　　**314/368-2100**
Division of Geological and Land Survey
Department Natural Resources
P.O. Box 250
Rolla 65401-0250

Disposal (RCRA), Soils

Responsible for lead disposal and detection of lead in soils.

JOHN YOUNG, DIRECTOR　　　　　　　　　　　　**314/751-4810**
Division of Environmental Quality　　　　　　　**FAX: 314/751-9277**
Department of Natural Resources
205 Jefferson Street
Jefferson City 65101

Environmental (General), Disposal (RCRA), NDWRL

Responsible for environmental lead programs. Lead is regulated
via farm programs, public drinking water, water pollution control,
and air and waste management program.

TODD DAMROW, STATE EPIDEMIOLOGIST   406/444-3986
Preventative Health Services   **FAX: 406/444-2606**
Department of Health and Environmental Sciences
Cogswell Building
Helena 59620

Overall Lead Contact

Coordinates state activities regarding health aspects of lead;
currently no state program.

JOHN DOWNEY, PROGRAM COORDINATOR   800/354-6465
Childhood Lead Poisoning Prevention   **FAX: 406/723-7245**
14 Butte-Silver Bow Health Department
25 West Front
Butte 59701

*Overall Lead Contact, Abatement/Standards and Enforcement, Laboratories
(Medical), Laboratories (Environmental), Financing Projects, Grant(s)
Recipient, Inspections, Public Outreach, Screening, Surveillance*

The Butte Childhood Lead Poisoning Prevention Program is
funded by a grant from Atlantic Richfield Corp. We have begun
collecting blood lead data statewide and have hired a grant-
writing firm to write a grant for screening statewide from the
CDC.

ADRIAN HOWE, CHIEF
Occupational and Radiological Health Bureau
Department of Health and Environmental Sciences
Cogswell Building., Room A-113
Helena 59620

406/444-3671
FAX: 406/444-1374

Laboratories (Environmental), Grant(s) Recipient, Inspections, Occupational Safety and Health

> Program is awaiting EPA's model plan before implementing a certification program.

STEVE PILCHER, ADMINISTRATOR
Department of Health and Environmental Sciences
Cogswell Building
P.O. Box 200901
Helena 59620-0904

406/444-3948
FAX: 406/444-2606

Environmental (General), LCCA, Disposal (RCRA), NDWRL

> Coordinates environmental activities of lead poisoning for the state.

JOHN BLOSSER, LABORATORY DIRECTOR   402/471-2122
State Health Laboratory
3701 South 14th Street
Lincoln 68502-5317

Laboratories (Medical)

Responsible for blood lead screening analysis.

SCOTT PETERSON, SUPERVISOR OF COMPLIANCE   402/471-2541
Bureau of Environment and Health   FAX: 402/471-0383
Department of Health
301 Centennial Mall South
Lincoln 68508-2529

LCCA, NDWRL

Responsible for regulations concerning lead in drinking water.

ADI POUR, PH.D., TOXICOLOGIST   402/471-2541
Bureau of Environmental Health   FAX: 402/471-0383
Department of Health
301 Centennial Mall South
Lincoln 68508-2529

Environmental, Financing Projects, Inspections

Responsible for environmental hazard follow-up and inspections, following HUD guidelines.

Rita Westover, R.N., B.S.N.
Maternal and Child Health Division
Department of Health
301 Centennial Mall South, Box 95007
Lincoln 68508-5004

402/471-0197
FAX: 402/471-0383

Overall Lead Contact, Medical Contact, NDWRL, Screening

Coordinates lead activities within the state; monitors maternal and child health lead program in Douglas County. The state plans to initiate outreach to physicians on lead poisoning.

DAVID GOING, SENIOR INDUSTRIAL HYGIENIST　　　**702/687-5240**
Division of Enforcement for　　　　　　　　　　　　**FAX: 702/687-6305**
 Industrial Safety and Health
Department of Industrial Relations
1370 South Currey Street
Carson City 89710-0001

Abatement/Standards and Enforcement, Occupational Safety and Health

> Responsible for several programs, including lead and will
> coordinate activities if more lead related programs develop.

DONALD S. KWALICK, M.D., M.P.H.　　　　　　　**702/687-4740**
State Health Officer　　　　　　　　　　　　　　　**FAX: 702/687-5197**
Health Division
Department of Health
505 East King Street, Capitol Complex
Carson City 89710-0004

Medical Contact

> Medical consultant for the state's lead activities.

LUANA RITCH, PUBLIC HEALTH AND INFORMATION OFFICER　**702/687-4885**
Family Health Services
State Health Division
505 East King Street
Carson City 89710-0004

Grant(s) Recipients, Inspections, Public Outreach, Screening

> Coordinates lead information activities in the state; seeking to
> initiate screening and inspections if funding becomes available.

BROOK DUPEE, ADMINISTRATOR
Bureau of Health Risk Assessment
Division of Public Health Services
6 Hazen Drive
Concord 03301-6501

603/271-4664
FAX: 603/271-3745

Overall Lead Contact, Occupational Safety and Health, Soils

Responsible for environmental inspections in private residences; provides recommendations or guidance to reduce blood lead levels; enforces abatement.

VERONICA MALMBERG, BUREAU CHIEF
Public Health Laboratories
Division of Public Health Services
6 Hazen Drive
Concord 03301-6501

603/271-4657
FAX: 603/271-3745

Laboratories (Medical), Laboratories (Environmental)

Overall management responsibility for Public Health Labs; the Inorganic Chemistry unit is responsible for blood lead testing of children and for OSHA purposes, as well as for environmental testing of soil, dust, paint, and pottery.

STERGIOS SPANOS, WASTE MANAGEMENT SPECIALIST
Department of Environmental Services
Waste Management Division
6 Hazen Drive
Concord 03301-6501

603/271-2942
FAX: 603/271-2456

Disposal (RCRA)

State enforcement program for solid and hazardous wastes; handling and disposal of lead contaminated debris.

RICHARD THAYER, JR., LEAD AND COPPER COORDINATOR   603/271-3139
Department of Environmental Services   **FAX: 603/271-3490**
Water Supply Engineering Bureau
6 Hazen Drive
P.O. Box 95
Concord 03301-6501

NDWRL

Responsible for implementation and enforcement of lead and copper rule.

MARTHA TURNER-WELLS, R.N., B.S.N., SUPERVISOR   603/271-4507
Childhood Lead Poisoning Prevention   **FAX: 603/271-3745**
Division of Public Health Services
6 Hazen Drive
Concord 03301-6501

Abatement/Standards and Enforcement, Inspections, Medical Contact, Public Outreach, Screening, Surveillance, Training/Certification/Accreditation, Grant(s) Recipient

Coordinates state program; state developing legislative task force on abatement, training, and certification; lead poisoning is a reportable disease; state is doing outreach to medical practitioners on lead poisoning.

JAMES A. BROWNLEE, M.P.H., DIRECTOR   **609/984-2193**
Environmental Health Services   **FAX: 609/984-2192**
Department of Health
CN 360
Trenton 08628

Training/Certification/Accreditation, Environmental

> Director of agency responsible for lead program. A training and
> certification program will be in place in one year.

JOAN COOK LUCKHARDT, PH.D., DIRECTOR, PSYCHIATRY   **609/782-6034**
Lead Poisoning Prevention   **FAX: 908/329-3429**
Education and Training Project
University of Medicine and Dentistry, NJSOM
301 South Central Plaza and Laurel Road
Stratford 08084

Public Outreach, Grant(s) Recipient

> Directs a statewide educational program on lead poisoning which
> designs and implements a public information campaign about the
> dangers of lead poisoning and encourage people to take personal
> responsibility to reduce lead exposure in their lives and in their
> community; provides technical assistance to local communities to
> develop lead education programs and to train outreach workers
> and cross-train health and housing professionals.

BARBARA GERWEL, M.D., RESEARCH SCIENTIST 609/984-1863
Epidemiology, Environment and OHS
Department of Health
John Fitch Plaza, CN 360
Trenton 08625

Occupational Safety and Health, Surveillance

Coordinates state occupational lead surveillance project, which
includes the collection of laboratory and physician case reports on
lead toxicity, medical consultations to affected workers and their
physicians, industrial hygiene evaluations at workplaces
identified as sources of exposure, and educational mailings to
affected individuals and their employers and physicians. The state
department of health requires laboratory reporting of blood lead
levels in adults equal to or greater than 25 µg/dL.

ROBERT HAUG, DIRECTOR 609/633-8161
Lead-Paint Abatement in Housing **FAX: 609/633-8084**
Department of Community Affairs
Division of Housing
CN 051
Trenton 08625-0051

Abatement/Standards and Enforcement

Responsible for abatement activities for community affairs.

STEPHEN JENNISS, DIRECTOR 609/292-8373
Environmental and Chemical Laboratories **FAX: 609/292-5201**
Department of Health
John Fitz Plaza, CN 360
Trenton 08625-0360

Laboratories (Medical), Laboratories (Environmental)

Responsible for blood lead and environmental lead analyses.

KEVIN MCNALLY, COORDINATOR
Childhood Lead Poisoning Prevention
Department of Health
363 West State Street, CN 364
Trenton 08625-0364

609/292-5666
FAX: 609/292-3580

Financing Projects, Grant(s) Recipient, Public Outreach, Screening, Surveillance

> Coordinates state childhood lead poisoning program; most activities through local health departments. Program provides technical assistance, consultation, financial assistance, and outreach to local health programs.

NANCY MURPHY, NURSE CONSULTANT
Childhood Lead Poisoning Prevention
Department of Health
363 West State Street, CN 364
Trenton 08625-0364

609/292-5666
FAX: 609/292-3580

Medical Contact

> Responsible for clinical case management components of the childhood lead poisoning program. Assists local agencies in identifying medical experts.

ROBERT TUCKER, PH.D., DIRECTOR
Division of Science and Research, NJEPE
401 East State Street, floor 1
Trenton 08625

609/984-6070
FAX: 609/292-7340

Overall Lead Contact, Environmental, Financing Projects, Disposal (RCRA), Soils

> Chairman of the Interagency Lead Task Force which includes all state agencies dealing with lead as well as representatives from other task forces and the private sector.

GENE VAN BENTHYSEN, PUBLIC HEALTH REPRESENTATIVE I   **609/292-5666**
Childhood Lead Poisoning Prevention Program   **FAX: 609/292-3580**
Department of Health
363 West State Street, CN 364
Trenton 08625-0364

Abatement/Standards and Enforcement, Inspections

> Responsible for the environmental components of the childhood
> lead poisoning prevention program.

LEAH ZISKIN, M.D., M.S., DEPUTY COMMISSIONER   **609/292-7836**
State Department of Health
CN 360
Trenton 08625-0360

Overall Lead Contact

> Lead contact for the Department of Health.

STEVE CARY, BUREAU CHIEF   **505/827-2929**
Groundwater Protection and Remediation   **FAX: 505/827-2965**
Environment Department
1190 Saint Francis Drive
P.O. Box 26110
Santa Fe 87502-0110

Environment, Inspection, Disposal, Soils

> Responsible for environmental investigation to identify problems
> and make recommendations for solutions. Lead is one of many
> hazardous wastes regulated.

ROBERT GALLEGOS, PROGRAM MANAGER   **505/827-2778**
Drinking Water Section   **FAX: 505/827-2965**
Environment Department
1190 Saint Francis Drive
P.O. Box 26110
Santa Fe 87502-0110

Overall Lead Contact, LCCA, NDWRL

> Responsible for detection of lead in drinking water.

MARIA GOLDSTEIN, M.D., DISTRICT HEALTH OFFICER   **505/841-4100**
1111 Standford Drive, N.E.
P.O. Box 25846
Albuquerque 87125

Medical Contact

> Medical consultant for the state's lead poisoning program.

DANIEL MERIANS, LEAD PROGRAM COORDINATOR   **505/827-0006**
Division of Epidemiology   **FAX: 505/827-0013**
Evaluation and Planning
Department of Health
P.O. Box 26110
Santa Fe 87502-0110

Overall Lead Contact, Grant(s) Recipient, Screening, Surveillance, Public Outreach

> Received CDC surveillance grant to screen children for lead. Organized pilot project in 10 communities to screen Medicaid and EPSDT children and to provide environmental follow-up.

DR. JOHN MEYER, CHEMISTRY BUREAU CHIEF   **505/841-2500**
Scientific Laboratory Division   **FAX: 505/841-2543**
Department of Health
P.O. Box 4700
Albuquerque 87196-4706

Laboratories (Environmental), Laboratories (Medical)

> Responsible for blood lead analysis.

MICHAEL D. COHEN, M.D., DIRECTOR
Bureau of Child and Adolescent Health
Department of Health
Empire State Plaza
Corning Tower, Rm 765
Albany 12237-0618

518/474-2084
FAX: 518/473-8673

Medical Contact

> Responsible for the overall administration of the state's lead poisoning program.

NANCY KIM, PH.D., DIRECTOR
Division of Environmental Assessment
Department of Health
2 University Place
Albany 12203

518/458-6438
FAX: 518/458-6434

Soils

> Responsible for detection of lead in soils.

DAVID MEAD, PROGRAM RESEARCH SPECIALIST III
Community Sanitation and Food Protection
Department of Health
2 University Place
Albany 12203

518/458-6706
FAX: 518/458-6732

Abatement/Standards and Enforcement, Financing Projects, Inspections

> Responsible for abatement and inspection standards and activities.

PATRICK PARSONS, PH.D., FRSC DIRECTOR   **518/474-5475**
Lead Poisoning Laboratory   **FAX: 518/473-2895**
Wadsworth Center for Labs and Research
Department of Health
P.O. Box 509
Albany 12201-0509

Laboratories (Medical), Laboratories (Environmental), Grant(s) Recipient

> Directs state proficiency testing program for blood lead and
> erythrocyte protoporphyrin (EP) laboratory accreditation for New
> York state OSHA and CLIA '88 purposes. Provides quality control
> materials for blood lead, urine lead, and EP to other state
> laboratories.

JAMES RAUCCI, PROGRAM ADMINISTRATOR   **518/473-4602**
Childhood Lead Poisoning Program   **FAX: 518/473-8673**
Department of Health
208 Tower Building
Albany 12237

Abatement/Standards and Enforcement, Grant(s) Recipients, Inspections,
Public Outreach, Screening, Surveillance

> Coordinates the local services portion of the state's lead poisoning
> prevention programs, including screening and follow-up
> activities. The state is moving into the second year of
> implementing revised lead guidelines, which includes providing
> blood lead measurements and follow-up intervention for children
> with blood lead levels at 10 µg/dL and above.

NANCY ROBINSON, M.P.H., PH.D., DIRECTOR   **518/473-4602**
Childhood Lead Poisoning Prevention Program   **FAX: 518/473-8673**
Bureau of Child and Adolescent Health
Department of Health
Corning Tower, Room 208
Albany 12237-0618

Overall Lead Contact, Screening, Surveillance, Public Outreach, Grant(s) Recipients, Financing Projects

> The state Childhood Lead Poisoning Prevention Program offers leadership and policy direction to 58 local health units and lead poisoning prevention programs. The state program supports the local programs with funding and technical assistance. The local programs are responsible for direct services for lead poisoning prevention, including lead screening, education, and case management of children with elevated lead levels.

GEORGE STASKO, SR. ENGINEER   **518/458-6743**
Public Water Supply Protection   **FAX: 518/458-6732**
Environmental Protection
Department of Health
2 University Place
Albany 12203

LCCA, NDWRL

> Responsible for detection of lead in drinking water.

ROBERT STONE, PH.D. 518/458-8228
Department of Health
2 University Place, Rm 155
Albany 12203-3399

Occupational Safety and Health

The state OSHA requires reporting if blood lead levels in workers arè over 25 µg/dL.

RICHARD SVENSON, DIRECTOR 518/458-6706
Community Sanitation and Food Protection FAX: 518/458-6732
Department of Health
2 University Place, Rm 404
Albany 12203-3313

Abatement/Standards and Enforcement, Environmental, Financing Projects, Inspections

Responsible for environmental activities on lead poisoning for the state. Program provides follow-up investigation, abatement guidance, and public outreach. Responsible for grants and financing certain local projects.

MARGARET BABB, ENVIRONMENTAL CHEMIST   **919/733-2178**
Hazardous Waste Section   **FAX: 919/733-4810**
Solid Waste Division
Department of Environment, Health and Natural Resources
P.O. Box 27687
Raleigh 27611-7687

Disposal (RCRA)

> Responsible for technical assistance in the management and
> disposal of hazardous waste, including lead

JOHN "PAT" CURRAN, C.I.H., MANAGER   **919/733-0820**
Asbestos Hazard Management Branch   **FAX: 919/233-8493**
Department of Environment, Health and Natural Resources
P.O. Box 27687
Raleigh 27611-7687

Training/Certification/Accreditation

> Responsible for establishing a comprehensive program involving
> training provider accreditation; certification of workers,
> supervisors, inspectors/risk assessors, and project designers; and
> the authorization of abatement projects. If passed by the General
> Assembly it will be effective May 1, 1994.

JAMES E. GEDDIE, PH.D., STAFF INDUSTRIAL HYGIENIST   **919/733-9690**
Department of Labor   **FAX: 919/733-0952**
Division of Occupational Safety and Health
413 North Salisbury Street
Raleigh 27603-1361

Occupational Safety and Health

> Enforcement of OSHA standards.

HORACE GRAHAM, ACTING CHIEF   919/733-3937
Newborn Screening/Clinical Chemistry   FAX: 919/733-8695
Department of Environment, Health and Natural Resources
306 North Wilmington Street.
P.O. Box 28047
Raleigh 27611-8047

Laboratories (Medical)

Responsible for blood lead analysis.

JAMES HAYES, MANAGER   919/733-9933
Lead Investigation and Abatement   FAX: 919/715-3227
Environmental Health
Department of Environment, Health and Natural Resources
P.O. Box 27687
Raleigh 27611-7687

Overall Lead Contact, Abatement/Standards and Enforcement, Inspections, Public Outreach

The lead investigation and abatement program provides environmental follow-up for reported cases of elevated blood lead levels in children and for schools or day care centers reasonably suspected of exposing children to lead. This includes education and outreach as well as enforcement of abatement standards where exposures have occurred.

LEBEED KADY, ENVIRONMENTAL ENGINEER   919/733-2178
Hazardous Waste Section   FAX: 919/733-4810
Solid Waste Division
Department of Environment, Health and Natural Resources
P.O. Box 27687
Raleigh 27611-7687

Disposal (RCRA)

Responsible for waste disposal regulation.

RONALD H. LEVINE, M.D., STATE HEALTH DIRECTOR   **919/733-4984**
Department of Environment,   **FAX: 919/733-0513**
  Health and Natural Resources
P.O. Box 27687
Raleigh 27611-7687

Medical Contact

Medical director for state for lead activities.

CHRIS LOVELACE, INDUSTRIAL HYGIENE CONSULTANT   **919/733-0820**
Asbestos Hazard Management   **FAX: 919/733-8493**
Environment, Health, and Natural Resources
P.O. Box 27687
Raleigh 27611-7687

Training/Certification/Accreditation

Responsible for training and certification standards.

LINDA MANN, ENFORCEMENT UNIT SUPERVISOR   **919/733-2178**
Hazardous Waste Section   **FAX: 919/733-4810**
Solid Waste Division
Department of Environment, Health and Natural Resources
P.O. Box 27687
Raleigh 27611-7687

Disposal (RCRA)

Responsible for disposal of lead-based wastes.

ROGER L. MCDANIEL JR., PH.D., CHIEF   919/733-7308
Environmental Sciences Section   FAX: 919/733-8695
Department of Environment, Health and Natural Resources
P.O. Box 28047
Raleigh 27611-8047

Laboratories (Environmental)

Responsible for environmental lead analysis.

ED NORMAN, PUBLIC HEALTH EPIDEMIOLOGIST   919/733-0385
Maternal and Child Health   FAX: 919/733-2997
Department of Environment, Health, and Natural Resources
P.O. Box 27687
Raleigh 27611-7687

Overall Lead Contact, Public Outreach, Screening, Surveillance

Coordinates medical follow-up and case management. Lead poisoning is a reportable disease if above 25 µg/dL.

WILLIAM S. SERVICE, INDUSTRIAL HYGIENIST   919/733-3410
Epidemiology   FAX: 919/733-9555
Department of Environment, Health and Natural Resources
P.O. Box 27687
Raleigh 27611-7687

Occupational Safety and Health

Responsible for occupational exposures that result in childhood exposure (e.g., a parent bringing home lead on clothing or body). Conduct surveys at exposure source (industry).

WALLACE E. VENRICK, CHIEF   **919/733-2321**
Public Water Supply Section   **FAX: 919/715-3242**
Division of Environmental Health
Department of Environment, Health and Natural Resources
P.O. Box 29536
Raleigh 27626-0536

LCCA, NDWRL

Responsible for regulations concerning lead in drinking water.

DAVID CUNNINGHAM, DIRECTOR   **701/224-2493**
Maternal and Child Health   **FAX: 701/224-4727**
Department of Health and Consolidated Laboratories
600 East Boulevard, Capitol Building
Bismarck 58505-0200

Overall Lead Contact, Screening, Surveillance

> Conducted two lead screening programs in high risk areas
> through Title V MCH funds; discovered low lead toxicity; no
> inspections needed. One screening in the eastern part of the state
> is being planned. Lead poisoning is a reportable disease.

DAVE GLATT, ACTING DIRECTOR   **701/221-6140**
Chemistry Division   **FAX: 701/221-6145**
Department of Health and Consolidated Laboratories
2635 East Main
P.O. Box 937
Bismarck 58502-0937

Laboratories (Medical), Laboratories (Environmental)

> Blood lead screening analysis is available through the state MCH
> program. Some environmental lead testing (drinking water, soil
> and paint) has occurred, but not on a routine basis.

STEVE MCDONOUGH, M.D., CHIEF   **701/224-2493**
Department of Health and Consolidated Laboratories   **FAX: 701/224-4727**
600 East Boulevard, Capitol Building
Bismarck 58505-0200

Medical Contact, Surveillance

> Responsible for state medical activities regarding lead, and
> receives reports of elevated blood lead levels.

FRANCIS SCHWINDT, CHIEF, ENVIRONMENTAL HEALTH   **701/221-5150**
Department of Health and Consolidated Laboratories **FAX: 701/221-5200**
P.O. Box 5520
Bismarck 58502-5520

Abatement/Standards and Enforcement, Laboratories (Medical), Environmental, Laboratories (Environmental), Inspections, Disposal (RCRA), NDWRL, Soils

Responsible for state environmental activities regarding lead.

DARLENE BANEY, LEAD PROGRAM COORDINATOR   **614/752-8452**
Maternal and Child Health   **FAX: 614/644-9850**
Pediatric and Adolescent Health Services Unit
Department of Health
246 North High Street
Columbus 43266-0118

Medical Contact, Public Outreach, Screening

> Have developed and funded four regional resource centers to
> routinely visit counties in their region to provide and develop
> education programs, probes, protocols, etc. Sponsors lead
> awareness week and the annual state lead conference. Information
> clearinghouse being developed, as are education modules.

RICHARD BUNNER, PROGRAM ADMINISTRATOR   **614/466-5332**
Division of Maternal and Child Health   **FAX: 614/644-9850**
Department of Health
246 North High Street
Columbus 43266-0001

Overall Lead Contact, Financing Projects, Grant(s) Recipient, Public Outreach,
Screening

> Coordinates the CDC program grant; provides technical
> assistance, financial assistance, and consultations to the state's
> three regional lead programs. Screening provided to Medicaid and
> low income children through variety of sources. Lead poisoning is
> not a reportable disease.

DAN CHATFIELD, PROGRAM COORDINATOR
Environmental Health
Department of Health
246 North High Street
Columbus 43266-0588

614/644-8649
FAX: 614/644-1909

Abatement/Standards and Enforcement, Inspections, LCCA

Responsible for environmental assessment in homes with children and for identifying children with elevated blood levels; provides soil and dust sampling analysis. Have drafted, but not implemented, rules and regulations on abatement standards and training certifications.

MARY LOU DITOMMASO, SURVEILLANCE COORDINATOR
Maternal and Child Health
Department of Health
246 North High Street
Columbus 43266-0118

614/466-5332
FAX: 614/644-9850

Laboratories (Medical), Laboratories (Environmental), Screening, Surveillance

Responsible for blood lead and environmental lead analyses.

CYNTHIA FRENCH, CDC LEAD GRANTS MANAGER
Public Health Advisor
Maternal and Child Health
Department of Health
246 North High Street
Columbus 43266-0118

614/466-5332
FAX: 614/644-9850

Financing Projects, Grant(s) Recipients

CDC technical assistant for the state.

THOMAS J. HALPIN, M.D, M.P.H., CHIEF 614/466-0302
Division of Preventive Medicine FAX: 614/644-8526
Department of Health
246 North High Street
Columbus 43266-0588

Laboratories (Medical)

Responsible for blood lead analysis.

PHILLIP HYDE, PROGRAM SPECIALIST 614/644-1894
Environmental Health/SEHS FAX: 614/644-1909
Department of Health
246 North High Street
Columbus 43266-0588

Inspections, Public Outreach

Conducts training for local health departments regarding all
environmental lead poisoning activities. Assists in providing
environmental education to the public, to private and public
agencies, and to out-of-state public and private agencies.

EDWARD KITCHEN, ENVIRONMENTAL MANAGER 614/644-2956
Hazardous Waste Management FAX: 614/644-2329
Environmental Protection Agency
1800 Watermark Drive
P.O. Box 1049
Columbus 43266-0149

Environmental, Disposal (RCRA), Soils

Responsible for environmental section of state's lead program,
including lead in soils and water.

KIRK LEIFHEIT, ENVIRONMENTAL MANAGER
Drinking and Ground Water
Environmental Protection Agency
1800 Watermark Drive
P.O. Box 1049
Columbus 43266-0149

614/644-2752
FAX: 614/644-2329

NDWRL

Responsible for supervising the drafting of the state's Lead and Copper Rule. Contact for information concerning compliance by public water systems in the state with the Lead and Copper Rule.

NAN MIGLIOZZI
Bureau of Occupational Health
Department of Health
246 North High Street
P.O. Box 118
Columbus 43266-0588

614/466-4183

Occupational Safety and Health

Responsible for determining lead exposure in occupational settings.

B. KIM MORTENSEN, PH.D., CHIEF
Bureau of Epidemiology and Toxicology
Department of Health
246 North High Street
P.O. Box 118
Columbus 43266-0118

614/466-5599
FAX: 614/644-7740

Environmental, Screening, Surveillance

Responsible for collecting data on lead-poisoned individuals for epidemiological purposes.

KATHY PEPPE, ACTING CHIEF
Division of Maternal and Child Health
P.O. Box 118
Columbus 43266-0118

614/466-3263
FAX: 614/644-8526

Overall Lead Contact, Medical Contact

Coordinates several programs, including lead poisoning
prevention; also medical consultant for programs.

NANCY PEES COLEMAN, PH.D., TOXICOLOGIST   **405/271-5220**
Environmental Health Services   **FAX: 405/271-7339**
Department of Health
1000 N.E. 10th Street
Oklahoma City 73117-1299

*Overall Lead Contact, Abatement/Standards and Enforcement,
Training/Certification/Accreditation*

> Responsible for abatement activities and any training or
> certification that may become mandatory. The program has
> developed strategies for childhood screening programs and
> reduction of lead levels in lead contaminated communities. The
> state has a lead task force that determines the activities the state
> undertakes on lead.

MONTE ELDERS, SR. ENVIRONMENTAL SPECIALIST   **405/271-8060**
Environmental Health Services   **FAX: 405/271-7339**
Department of Health
1000 N.E. 10th Street
Oklahoma City 73117-1299

Inspections, Public Outreach

> Coordinates public outreach on site specific lead projects. Provides
> consultation on inspections of housing and environmental
> sampling.

EDD RHOADES, M.D., M.P.H., DIRECTOR PEDIATRICS   **405/271-4471**
Maternal and Child Health Service   **FAX: 405/271-6199**
Department of Health
1000 N.E. 10th Street
Oklahoma City 73117-1299

Overall Lead Contact, Grant(s) Recipients, Medical Contact, Screening,
Surveillance

> Limited childhood blood lead screening available to high risk
> children through state health department. Blood lead levels of 10
> µg/dL are reportable. ATSDR site specific screening project
> funded for Bartlesville.

GLEN WHEAT   **405/271-7160**
Solid Waste Management   **FAX: 405/271-7339**
1000 N.E. 10th Street
Oklahoma City 73117-1212

Disposal

> Responsible for review and approval of disposal plans for non-
> hazardous lead-contaminated materials.

MARGOT BARNETT, MANAGER　　　　　　　　**503/731-4025**
Occupational Health Epidemiology
Health Division
State Office Bldg.
800 N.E. Oregon Street, Ste. 730
Portland 97232

Occupational Health and Safety, Public Outreach, Surveillance, Grant(s)
Recipient, Screening

> Responsible for blood lead testing and screening. The state health
> division requires laboratory reporting if blood lead levels are
> greater than 10 µg/dL in children 17 years old or younger and 25
> µg/dL in adults 18 years old or older.

> Performs epidemiologic case follow-up of elevated blood lead
> levels as part of surveillance activities. The agency may work with
> local health agencies and employers (on a consultative basis), or
> make referral to Oregon OSHA on a case-by-case basis.

CHARLES BROKOPP, ASSISTANT ADMINISTRATOR　　　　**503/229-5882**
Office of Laboratories
Health Division
1717 Southwest 10th Street
Portland 97201

Laboratories (Medical), Laboratories (Environmental)

> Responsible for laboratory licensing and certification. Program
> also responsible for supervision and enforcement of laboratories,
> but no supervision specifically for blood lead screening.

CHRIS JOHNSON, COORDINATOR   503/248-5240
Childhood Lead Poisoning Prevention Project   **FAX: 503/248-3407**
Health Division
426 S.W. Stark Street
Portland 97204

Overall Lead Contact, Financing Projects, Screening, Public Outreach

> Coordinates program which includes screening, the lead registry, and care management and environmental follow-up. Does inspections of homes with children with elevated blood lead of 20 μg/dL or above. Responds to questions by public regarding lead poisoning.

KENNETH KAUFFMAN   503/731-4015
Environmental Health Specialist   **FAX: 503/731-4077**
Environmental Toxicology
Health Division
800 N.E. Oregon Street, Ste. 608
Portland 97232

Abatement/Standards and Enforcement, Inspections, LCCA, NDWRL, Soils, Surveillance, Environmental

> Responds to public inquiries about residential lead exposure and lead toxicology. Provides guidance on lead abatement and testing.

JOHN POMPEI, ADMINISTRATOR   503/378-3272
OSHA   **FAX: 503/378-5729**
Department of Insurance and Finance
21 Labor and Industries Building
Salem 97310

Occupational Safety and Health

> Administers the Oregon Safe Employment Act and enforces the Oregon occupational safety and health rules. (Rules on lead are found in OAR 437, Division 2, Subdivision Z.)

GERALD B. CURTIS, COORDINATOR   **717/783-8451**
Childhood Lead Poisoning Prevention(CLPPP)   **FAX: 717/783-3794**
Department of Health
P.O. Box 90, Rm 725
Harrisburg 17108-0090

*Overall Lead Contact, Financing Projects, Inspections, Public Outreach,
Screening , Surveillance*

Coordinates lead poisoning prevention program and state-funded
local CLPPP projects.

JAMES FOX, M.D.   **717/787-1708**
Division of Environmental Health   **FAX: 717/783-3797**
Department of Health
P.O. Box 90, Room 1020
Harrisburg 17108

Medical Contact, Surveillance

Medical consultant on environmental health issues, including
blood lead surveillance.

JUDY GOSTIN, INDUSTRIAL HYGIENIST   **717/787-1708**
Environmental Health   **FAX: 717/783-3794**
Department of Health
P.O. Box 90, Room 1020
Harrisburg 17108

Occupational Safety and Health

Coordination of occupational health activities, including reviews
of adult (occupational) blood lead reports submitted to the
department.

JAMES N. LOGUE, PH.D., M.P.H., DIRECTOR   717/787-1708
Division of Environmental Health   **FAX: 717/787-3794**
Department of Health
P.O. Box 90, Rm 1020
Harrisburg 17108-0090

Surveillance

> Responsible for receiving all reports of elevated blood lead levels from laboratories certified by the department of health to do the testing.

FRED MARROCCO, CHIEF   717/787-0122
Division of Drinking Water Management   **FAX: 717/772-3249**
Department of Environmental Resources
P.O. Box 8467
Harrisburg 17105-8467

NDWRL

> Responsible for detection of lead in drinking water.

DEBORAH ROTZ, LEAD CONTROL COORDINATOR   717/787-0122
Division of Drinking Water Management   **FAX: 717/772-3249**
Department of Environmental Resources
P.O. Box 8467
Harrisburg 17105-8467

Environmental, LCCA

> Responsible for developing state lead and copper drinking water regulations; contact person for the state lead ban law (Act 33), which bans the sale and use of certain leaded materials used in plumbing systems.

M. Jeffery Shoemaker, Ph.D., Acting Director　　　　**215/363-8500**
Division of Chemistry and Toxicology　　　　　　**FAX: 215/436-3346**
Department of Health
P.O. Box 500
Exton 19341-0500

Laboratories (Medical)

> Responsible for blood lead analysis and for setting standards
> regarding blood lead samples for all laboratories in the state.
> Laboratories are required to report elevated blood lead levels.

Helen Shuman, Director　　　　　　　　　　　　**717/783-8451**
Childhood Lead Poisoning Prevention (CLPPP)
Department of Health
P.O. Box 90, Rm 725
Harrisburg 17110-2194

Overall Lead Contact, Financing Projects, Inspections, Public Outreach,
Screening, Surveillance

> Directs state funded local CLPPP projects; program involves
> screening, follow-up, case management, environmental
> investigation, referral for treatment, community outreach,
> prevention and education, and enforcement of local ordinances.
> Currently developing demonstration project for lead-based paint
> hazard reduction.

LYNN BOULAY, C.I.H., TOXICOLOGIST   **401/277-3424**
Environmental Health Risk Assessment   **FAX: 401/277-6953**
Department of Health
206 Cannon Hill
Providence 02908-5097

Inspections, Grant(s) Recipient

> Responsible for environmental and public/private residence inspection if elevated blood lead levels are identified or if residence is in high risk area. Makes referrals if elevated blood lead is found in workers.

TED BURNS   **401/277-2808**
Division of Air and Hazardous Materials
Department of Environmental Management
261 Promenade Street
Providence 02908

Abatement/Standards and Enforcement

> Clean Air Act fugitive dust/exterior lead paint removal.

RON BUSH, SUPERVISING CHEMIST   **401/274-1011**
Department of Health
Chapin Laboratory Building
50 Orms Street
Providence 02904-2244

Laboratories (Medical)

> Responsible for blood lead analysis.

HARISH CHANDRA, M.D., M.P.H., EPIDEMIOLOGIST   **401/277-3424**
Office of Environmental Health Risk Assessment   **FAX: 401/277-6953**
Department of Health
206 Cannon Building, Three Capitol Hill
Providence 02908-5097

Surveillance

Collects surveillance data for epidemiological purposes.

THOMAS EPSTEIN, SUPERVISING ENGINEER   **401/272-2797**
Air and Hazardous Materials   **FAX: 401/277-2017**
Department of Environmental Management
291 Promenade Street
Providence 02908-5767

Disposal (RCRA)

Responsible for disposal of toxics, including lead.

CATHERINE O'MALLEY, COORDINATOR   **401/277-1185**
Childhood Lead Poisoning Control Program   **FAX: 401/277-1442**
Division of Family Health
Department of Health
3 Capitol Hill, Cannon Building, Room 302
Providence 02908-5097

*Overall Lead Contact, Grant(s) Recipients, Public Outreach, Screening,
Surveillance*

Responsible for screening, surveillance of high risk areas and
children, and clinical management.

PETER SIMON, M.D., M.P.H., ASSISTANT DIRECTOR   **401/277-1185**
Family Health   **FAX: 401/277-1442**
Department of Health
3 Capitol Hill, Cannon Building, Rm 302
Providence 02908-5097

Medical Contact

Responsible for all medical aspects of lead program.

JAMES SULLIVAN, PH.D., LABORATORIES   **401/274-1011**
Department of Health
Orms Street
Providence 02908

Laboratories (Medical), Laboratories (Environmental)

Responsible for blood lead and environmental lead analyses.

JUNE SWALLOW, P.E., CHIEF   **401/277-6867**
Drinking Water Quality Division
Department of Health
209 Cannon Building, 3 Capitol Hill
Providence 02908

NDWRL

Responsible for regulation of lead in drinking water.

ROBERT VANDERSLICE, PH.D., CHIEF   **401/277-3424**
Office of Environmental Health and Risk Assessment **FAX: 401/277-6953**
Department of Health
3 Capitol Hill
Providence 02908

Training/Certification/Accreditation, Public Outreach, Abatement/Standards and Enforcement, Soils

Responsible for the environmental component of the state's lead program.

ROBERT MARINO, M.D., M.P.H., DIRECTOR   803/737-4170
Division of Health Hazard Evaluation   FAX: 803/737-4171
Department of Health and Environmental Control
Robert Mills Complex
P.O. Box 101106
Columbia 29211

Medical Contact

Conducts adult lead poisoning surveillance; reports summaries to
NIOSH. Collaborates with South Carolina OSHA and Alcohol
Beverage Control Commission on investigations into adult lead
poisonings.

CHARLOTTE MCCREARY, NURSING CONSULTANT   803/737-4069
Children's Health   FAX: 803/737-4078
Department of Health and Environmental Control
2600 Bull Street
Columbia 29201-1708

Medical Contact

Serves as nursing consultant for screening activities in the state;
majority of screening done by local health agencies.

SAM MCNUTT, DIRECTOR   803/734-5072
Division of Training and Consumer Health
Bureau Environmental Health
2600 Bull Street
Columbia 29201-1708

*Abatement/Standards and Enforcement, Environmental, Inspections, Public
Outreach*

Responsible for abatement guidelines and environmental
investigation on dwellings and other facilities. Provides
educational materials to local health agencies.

PAM MEYER, M.S.P.H., DIRECTOR
Childhood Lead Poisoning Prevention
Department of Health and Environmental Control
426 North Robert Mills Building
P.O. Box 101106
Columbia 29223

803/737-4061
FAX: 803/734-3255

Overall Lead Contact, Screening, Surveillance

> Coordinates statewide screening activities for children older than 72 months; most childhood lead screening is being done at the local health departments. The state health department coordinates reports of elevated blood lead levels. Lead poisoning greater than 10 µg/dL is reportable for children.

DAVID PRICE, MANAGER
Facilities Compliance Section
Drinking Water Quality
Department of Health and Environmental Control
2600 Bull Street
Columbia 29201

803/734-5341
FAX: 803/734-4661

LCCA, NDWRL

> Responsible for regulations concerning lead in drinking water regulations.

DAVID WILSON, DIRECTOR
Division of Hazardous
  and Infectious Waste Management
Department of Health and Environmental Control
2600 Bull Street
Columbia 29201

803/734-5173
FAX: 803/734-5199

Disposal (RCRA)

> Responsible for the disposal of lead based wastes.

DARRON C. BUSCH, ADMINISTRATOR   605/773-3754
Office of Drinking Water
Joe Foss Building
523 East Capitol Avenue
Pierre 57501-3182

LCCA, NDWRL

Responsible for detection of lead in drinking water.

KEVIN FORSCH, DIRECTOR   605/773-3364
Office of Health Protection   FAX: 605/773-5904
Department of Health
445 East Capitol Avenue
Pierre 57501-3182

Overall Lead Contact, Abatement/Standards and Enforcement, Environmental, Public Outreach, Screening, Surveillance

No formal lead program; however, state will be conducting several screening projects through cooperation with Centers for Disease Control. Currently, lead poisoning is not a reportable disease.

MIKE SMITH, ACTING DIRECTOR   605/773-3368
State Health Laboratory   FAX: 605/773-6129
Department of Health
500 East Capitol Avenue
Pierre 57501

Laboratories (Medical), Laboratories (Environmental)

No blood lead screening at the present time. If lead poisoning becomes an issue the state laboratory will have blood lead screening capabilities. Environmental lead testing is available.

SANDRA VAN GERPEN, M.D., M.P.H.
Assistant Secretary
Health and Medical Services
Department of Health
445 East Capitol Avenue
Pierre 57501

605/773-3737
FAX: 605/773-5683

Medical Contact

Medical consultant for lead program.

STEPHEN BLACKBURN, DIRECTOR   615/741-7206
Department of Health, Food and General Sanitation   FAX: 615/352-2286
C-1 136 Cordell Hull Building
Nashville 37247-3901

Inspections

Responsible for environmental follow-up when lead is identified.

W. DAVID DRAUGHON, JR., DIRECTOR   615/532-0152
Division of Water Supply   FAX: 615/532-0231
Department of Environment and Conservation
L and C Tower
401 Church Street, 6th floor
Nashville 37243-1549

Overall Lead Contact, LCCA, NDWRL

Public water systems under SDWA School LCCA. Responsible for detection of lead in drinking water.

MICHAEL KIMBERLY, P.H., M.P.H., C.L.D., DIRECTOR   615/262-6300
Laboratory Services   FAX: 615/262-6393
Department of Health
630 Ben Allen Road
Nashville 37247-0801

Laboratories (Medical), Laboratories (Environmental)

Responsible for analysis of environmental samples when high blood lead levels in children have been identified.

ROBERT TAYLOR, D.V.M., M.P.H., DIRECTOR   615/741-5683
Childhood Lead Poisoning Prevention Program   FAX: 615/532-2286
Department of Health, Environmental Epidemiology
C1-130 Cordell Hull Building
Nashville 37247-4912

Overall Lead Contact, Abatement/Standards and Enforcement, Financing Projects, Grant(s) Recipients, Public Outreach, Screening, Surveillance, Training/Certification/Accreditation, Medical Contact

Coordinates state's lead program; provides support to local health programs for screening, environmental evaluations and follow-up, abatement, and education/training. Lead poisoning is reportable for all Medicaid eligible children through the HCFA- EPSDT program.

JEAN BRENDER, R.N., PH.D., DIRECTOR   **512/458-7269**
Environmental Epidemiology Program   **FAX: 512/458-7601**
Department of Health
1100 West 49th Street
Austin 78756

Grant(s) Recipients, Inspections, Surveillance

> Program is responsible for surveillance and follow-up of blood
> lead levels in workers that are at or above 40 µg/dL.

JERRY LAUDERDALE, DIRECTOR   **512/834-6600**
Occupational Health   **FAX: 512/834-6644**
Department of Health
1100 West 49th Street
Austin 78756-3194

Abatement/Standards and Enforcement, Inspections,
Training/Certification/Accreditation

> Responsible for abatement activities for the state. Has a list of
> abatement contractors for referral, but no specific training or
> certification.

DENNIS PERROTTA, DIRECTOR   **512/458-7268**
Division of Epidemiology   **FAX: 512/458-7601**
Department of Health
1100 West 49th Street
Austin 78756

Occupational Safety and Health

> The state OSHA requires reporting of blood lead levels at or above
> 40 µg/dL in workers.

DR. LINDA PRENTICE, DIRECTOR
Child Health Division
Bureau of Maternal and Child Health
1100 West 49th Street
Austin 78756-3101

512/458-7700
FAX: 512/458-7350

Overall Lead Contact, Medical Contact

Responsible for public and professional education.

DIANA SALZMAN, M.P.H.
Environmental Quality Specialist
Environmental Epidemiology Program
Department of Health
1100 West 49th Street
Austin 78756

512/458-7269
FAX: 512/458-7601

Inspections, Surveillance, Grant(s) Recipient

Received CDC grant to screen and study occupational lead
exposures; seeking funding to initiate childhood screening and
surveillance program.

CHARLES SWEET, PH.D., CHIEF
Bureau of Laboratories
Department of Health
1100 West 49th Street
Austin 78756-3194

512/458-7318
FAX: 512/458-7294

Laboratories (Medical), Laboratories (Environmental)

Responsible for blood lead and environmental lead analyses.

STEVE E. WALDEN, MANAGER
Monitoring and Enforcement
Water Utilities Division
Texas Water Commission
P.O. Box 13087
Austin 78711

512/908-6020
FAX: 512/908-6060

LCCA, NDWRL

Responsible for regulations concerning lead in drinking water.

DENISE E. BEAUDOIN, M.D., M.S.P.H., COORDINATOR   **801/538-6191**
Epidemiological Studies Program   **FAX: 801/538-6036**
Community Health Services
Bureau of Epidemiology
288 North 1460 West
P.O. Box 16660
Salt Lake City 84116-0660

Overall Lead Contact, Grant(s) Recipient, Surveillance

Blood lead levels of 15 µg/dL or greater are now reportable to the
state department of health. Clinical laboratories are required to
report cases of elevated blood lead levels on a quarterly basis.
These data will be used to determine risk factors for lead exposure
and the need for further follow-up.

WAYNE PIERCE, DIRECTOR   **801/584-8400**
Bureau of Environmental Chemistry and Toxicology   **FAX: 801/584-8486**
Laboratory Services
Health Department
46 North Medical Drive
Salt Lake City 84113-1105

Laboratories (Environmental), Laboratories (Medical)

Responsible for environmental lead analysis.

DANIEL SYMONIK, SUPERFUND SECTION MANAGER   **801/536-4100**
Environmental Response and Remediation   **FAX: 801/359-8853**
Department of Environmental Quality
1959 West North Temple
Salt Lake City 84116-3046

Environmental, Soils

Responsible for lead as a toxic substance in the environment.

WILLIAM BRESS, PH.D., STATE TOXICOLOGIST   802/863-7220
Division of Environmental Health   FAX: 802/863-7425
Department of Health
P.O. Box 70
Burlington 05402

Overall Lead Contact, Environmental, Inspections, Public Outreach, Screening

> Provides environmental investigation and case management to houses with children with elevated blood levels. Provides lead information to communities and individuals.

ROBERT HOUSEKNECHT, M.D., DIRECTOR   802/863-7240
Division of Epidemiology   FAX: 802/863-7425
Department of Health
P.O. Box 70
Burlington 05402-0070

Medical Contact, Surveillance

> Medical consultant for state program. Program collects data on blood lead levels. Lead poisoning is reportable above 10 µg/dL.

RAY MCCANDLESS, DIRECTOR   802/863-7332
Division of Occupational Health   FAX: 802/865-7745
Department of Health
108 Cherry Street
P.O. Box 70
Burlington 05402-0070

Occupational Safety and Health

> State follows the general industry standards set by federal OSHA.

JAY RUTHERFORD, P.E., DIRECTOR　　　　　　　**802/244-1562**
Water Supply Division　　　　　　　　　　　**FAX: 802/244-5141**
Agency of Natural Resources
103 South Main Street
Waterbury 05671-0404

NDWRL

Responsible for detection of lead in drinking water.

BURTON WILCKE, JR., DIRECTOR　　　　　　**802/863-7335**
Public Health Laboratory　　　　　　　　　**FAX: 802/863-7632**
Department of Health
195 Colchester Avenue
P.O. Box 1125
Burlington 05402-1125

Laboratories (Medical), Laboratories (Environmental)

Responsible for blood lead and environmental lead analyses.

BOBBY HILL, BUILDING CODE SUPERVISOR   **804/371-7160**
Code Enforcement Office   **FAX: 804/371-7092**
Department of Housing and Community Development
501 North Second Street
Richmond 23219-1321

Abatement/Standards and Enforcement, Public Housing

> Responsible for guidelines and regulations for new and existing residences.

EDWARD LEFEBVRE, DIRECTOR   **804/786-3767**
Consolidated Lab Services
Bureau of Chemistry
Richmond 23219-3691

Laboratories (Medical)

> Responsible for blood lead analysis.

EILEEN MANNIX, M.P.H., DIRECTOR   **804/786-7307**
Childhood Lead Poisoning Prevention Program   **FAX: 804/371-6031**
Maternal and Child Health
Department of Health
1500 East Main Street
Richmond 23218

Overall Lead Contact, Financing Projects, Grant(s) Recipient, Public Outreach

> Responsible for state lead program; lead poisoning reportable as of April, 1993; CDC grant recipient.

LEONARD VANCE, ASSOCIATE PROFESSOR   **804/786-9785**
Department of Preventative Medicine
P.O. Box 212
Richmond 23298

Environmental, Training/Certification/Accreditation

Responsible for environmental component of state's lead program.
Provides training to abatement professionals.

JANET ABBETT, MANAGER   **206/664-8154**
Housing Rehabilitation Program, Housing Division   **FAX: 206/586-5880**
Department of Community Development
P.O. Box 48300
906 Columbia Street Station
Olympia 98504-8300

Abatement/Standards and Enforcement, Public Housing

> Responsible for state and federally subsidized public housing.
> HUD guidelines are enforced.

JAC DAVIES, CHIEF   **206/361-2910**
Office of Environmental Chemistry Laboratory   **FAX: 206/361-2904**
Public Health Laboratories
Department of Health
1610 N.E. 150th Street
Seattle 98155-7224

Laboratories (Medical), Laboratories (Environmental)

> Responsible for blood lead testing and environmental, soil, and
> paint analysis.

JIM FERNALD, INDUSTRIAL HYGIENIST   **206/956-5428**
HART Program   **FAX: 206/956-5672**
Department of Labor and Industries
P.O. Box 44610
805 Plum Street, S.E.
Olympia 98504-4610

Occupational Safety and Health

> Responsible for enforcement of lead standards.

JIM HUDSON, SECTION HEAD
Technical Services Section
Division of Drinking Water
Department of Health
Airdustrial Center, Bldg. 3
P.O. Box 47822
Olympia 98504-7822

206/753-9674
FAX: 206/586-5529

LCCA, NDWRL

Responsible for regulations concerning lead in drinking water.

JOEL KAUFMAN, M.D., M.P.H.
Safety and Health Assessment and Research Program
Department of Labor and Industries SHARP
P.O. Box 44330
Olympia 98504-4330

206/956-5669
FAX: 206/956-5672

Medical Contact, Surveillance

Responsible for adult surveillance and occupational prevention activities.

JOHN KOBAYASHI, M.D., ACTING DIRECTOR
Office of Epidemiology
Department of Health
Mailstop: K17-9
Seattle 98155

206/361-2831
FAX: 206/361-2930

Surveillance

Responsible for surveillance of childhood lead poisoning.

Vern Meinz, Environmental Engineer　　　206/459-6687
Solid and Hazardous Waste　　　FAX: 206/438-7759
Department of Ecology
P.O. Box 47600
Olympia 98504-7600

Disposal (RCRA)

Responsible for the disposal of lead-based wastes.

David F. Nash, Public Health Advisor　　　206/753-2730
Office of Toxic Substances　　　FAX: 206/586-4499
Department of Health
Airdustrial Center, Building 4
P.O. Box 47825
Olympia 98504-7825

Public Outreach

Responsible for lead publications and answering basic questions.

Steve Robb, Supervisor　　　206/438-3057
Technical Support　　　FAX: 206/438-3050
Toxic Cleanup Program
Department of Ecology
P.O. Box 47600
Olympia 98504-7600

Environmental, Soils

The Toxic Cleanup Program administers the state hazardous
waste site cleanup program, similar to the federal Superfund
program. Cleanup standards are risk-based.

JAMES WHITE, SECTION HEAD   **206/753-2556**
Environmental Health Assessment Section   **FAX: 206/586-4499**
Office of Toxic Substances
Department of Health
Mailstop 7825
Airdustrial Center, Building 4
Olympia 98504-7825

Overall Lead Contact, Abatement/Standards and Enforcement, Grant(s)
Recipients, Training/Certification/Accreditation, Public Outreach

Responsible for coordination of the state's lead activities.

CATHY HAYES, SUPERVISOR   304/558-0197
Environmental Chemistry Laboratory   FAX: 304/558-1362
Office of Laboratory Services
151 11th Avenue
South Charleston 25303-1114

Laboratories (Medical), Laboratories (Environmental)

> Responsible for blood lead and environmental lead analyses.

WILLIAM PINNELL, R.S., CHIEF   304/558-2981
Asbestos/Lead Control Program   FAX: 304/558-0691
Bureau of Public Health
815 Quarrier Street, Ste. 4
Charleston 25301-2616

Abatement/Standards and Enforcement, Training/Certification/Accreditation

> Responsible for lead environmental assessments and lead
> abatement, training, certification, and licensing.

BOBBY PRITT, SANITARIAN   304/558-2981
Environmental Engineering   FAX: 304/558-0691
Bureau of Public Health
815 Quarrier Street
Charleston 25301-2616

LCCA, NDWRL

> Responsible for regulations concerning lead in drinking water.

HENRY ANDERSON, M.D.
Bureau of Public Health
1414 East Washington Avenue, Room 96
Madison 53703-3044

608/266-1253
FAX: 608/267-3696

Medical Contact

Medical consultant and principal investigator for the CDC Lead
Poisoning Prevention Grant.

TERRY BURK, ASSISTANT SECTION CHIEF
Occupational Health Laboratory
Laboratory of Hygiene
979 Jonathan Drive
Madison 53713

608/263-8160
FAX: 608/263-6551

Laboratories (Environmental)

Responsible for conducting environmental lead analysis.

MARK CHAMBERLAIN, L.P.N.
Environmental Health Specialist
Bureau of Public Health
Department of Health and Social Services
1414 East Washington Avenue, Room 96
Madison 53703-3044

608/266-7897
FAX: 608/267-3696

Inspections, Abatement/Standards and Enforcement

Responsible for inspections, abatement guidelines, and education
of home owners; enforcement of state lead health regulations;
coordination of enforcement activities within various state
agencies.

MARGIE JOOSSE COONS, R.N. 608/267-0473
Bureau of Public Health FAX: 608/267-3696
1414 East Washington Avenue, Room 96
Madison 53703

Surveillance, Screening

> Responsible for any screening or surveillance activities.

REGINA COWELL, SUPERVISOR 608/267-2289
Certification and Training Unit FAX: 608/267-3696
Division of Health
1414 East Washington Avenue, Room 96
Madison 53703

Training/Certification/Accreditation

> The state is developing training course standards, accreditation of
> training providers, and certification of lead professionals.

CINDY DIEDRICH, ENVIRONMENTAL SPECIALIST 608/267-2451
Bureau of Water Supply FAX: 608/267-7664
Department of Natural Resources
P.O. Box 7921
Madison 53707

LCCA

> Responsible for lead found in public and private water supplies.

JODY DIEDRICH, R.N., M.S., PROGRAM COORDINATOR   **608/266-1826**
Bureau of Pubic Health   **FAX: 608/267-3696**
1414 East Washington Avenue, Room 96
Madison 53703-3044

Screening, Surveillance , Grant(s) Recipient

> CDC grant coordinator. Responsible for surveillance, screening, and case management activities for the state. Under state law, all blood lead levels of 25 µg/dL or more must be reported. This reporting requirement will be changed to 10 µg/dL to make it more consistent with the federal CDC guidelines of 1991. Also responsible for public outreach to physicians and nurses.

DEE HIGGINS, PUBLIC HEALTH NURSE   **608/267-3256**
Division of Health   **FAX: 608/267-3696**
Department of Health and Social Services
1414 East Washington Avenue
Madison 53703-3044

Grant(s) Recipient, Surveillance, Public Outreach

> Responsible for adult occupational lead surveillance. The program "Adult Lead Surveillance" is not a regulatory program; follow-up is educational. Companies are advised to call the Wisconsin OSHA consultation program for onsite work area consultation (private sector). Division of Health offers consultation to both private and public entities.

LARRY LANDSNESS, P.E., WATER SUPPLY ENGINEER   **608/267-7647**
Bureau of Water Supply   **FAX: 608/267-7664**
Department of Natural Resources
P.O. Box 7921
Madison 53707

NDWRL

> Responsible for detection of lead in drinking water.

JIM LUTZ, CHIEF   608/266-7731
Safety Section
Safety and Buildings
Labor and Human Relations
Department of Industry
201 East Washington Avenue
Madison 53703

Occupational Safety and Health

Enforces DILHR and OSHA regulations for public sector
employees. Federal OSHA provides regulation for the private
sector.

BILL OTTO, SUPERVISOR   608/266-9337
Health Hazard Evaluation Unit   FAX: 608/267-3696
Bureau of Public Health
1414 East Washington Avenue, Room 96
Madison 53703

Overall Lead Contact, Financing Projects

Responsible for CDC grant and HUD coordination.

JOSEPH SCHIRMER, EPIDEMIOLOGIST   608/266-5885
Public Health Educator   FAX: 608/267-3696
Bureau of Public Health
1414 East Washington Avenue, Room 96
Madison 53703-3044

Public Outreach

Responsible for environmental hazard reduction and assessments;
coordinates the environmental component of the state's lead
program; technical assistance for the CDC and HUD lead grants.
Also coordinates HUD funded lead abatement in private housing.

NOEL STANTON, CHEMIST
Toxicology
State Laboratory of Hygiene
465 Henry Mall
Madison 53706-1501

608/262-1146
FAX: 608/262-5494

Laboratories (Medical)

Responsible for blood lead analysis and urine lead, erythrocyte protoporpnyrin (EP), and ceramic leachate lead analysis. Administers the federally sponsored (with CDC and BMCHRD) blood lead and EP proficiency testing programs.

DON SWAILES, SAFE DRINKING WATER UNIT SUPERVISOR
Bureau of Water Supply
Department of Natural Resources
P.O. Box 7921
Madison 53707

608/266-7093
FAX: 608/267-7664

NDWRL

Responsible for detection of lead in drinking water.

BARBARA ZELLMER, CHIEF
Hazardous Waste
Department of Natural Resources
101 South Webster Street
P.O. Box 7921
Madison 53707-7921

608/266-7055
FAX: 608/267-2768

Disposal (RCRA), Soils

Responsible for disposal of toxics, including lead.

LARRY GOODMAY, PROGRAM MANAGER   307/777-6186
Genetics Program
Department of Health
Hathaway Building, 4th floor
Cheyenne 82002

Medical Contact, Screening

> Responsible for screening program initiated to identify level of
> lead poisoning problem within state.

JAMES HOLLADAY, INDUSTRIAL HYGIENIST   307/777-7786
Department of Employment   FAX: 307/777-5805
Occupational Health and Safety
Herschler Building 2E
Cheyenne 82002

Occupational Safety and Health

> Responsible for implementing occupational health and safety
> standards throughout the state.

HOWARD HUTCHINGS, MANAGER   307/777-7957
Preventive Medicine   FAX: 307/777-5402
Department of Health
Hathaway Building, Room 487
Cheyenne 82002

Overall Lead Contact, Environmental, Public Outreach

> The state does not have a formal lead prevention program.
> Provides public information, suggestions and referrals. Blood lead
> testing is handled by the Genetics Program in the Children's
> Health Division.

ROBERT ROSS, INDUSTRIAL HYGIENIST
Department of Employment
Occupational Health and Safety
Herschler Building 2E
Cheyenne 82002

307/777-7786
FAX: 307/777-5805

Occupational Safety and Health

Responsible for implementing occupational health and safety standards throughout the state of Wyoming.